THE BOOKMARK READING PROGRAM

PRIMARY READERS

Margaret Early, Elizabeth K. Cooper, Nancy Santeusanio, Marian Adell

Going Places,
Seeing People

Stories written especially for *Going Places, Seeing People*
by Elizabeth K. Cooper

HARCOURT BRACE JOVANOVICH, INC.

New York   *Chicago*   *San Francisco*   *Atlanta*   *Dallas*

ACKNOWLEDGMENTS: For permission to reprint copyrighted material, grateful acknowledgment is made to the following sources:

ATHENEUM PUBLISHERS: Adaptation of *The Story of Olaf* by James and Ruth McCrea, copyright © 1964 by James and Ruth McCrea.

THOMAS Y. CROWELL COMPANY: Adaptation of *Eagle Feather* by Clyde Robert Bulla, copyright © 1953 by Clyde Robert Bulla.

E. P. DUTTON & CO., INC.: "There Are So Many Ways of Going Places" by Leslie Thompson, from *Another Here and Now Story Book* by Lucy Sprague Mitchell, copyright 1937 by E. P. Dutton & Co., Inc.; renewal © 1965 by Lucy Sprague Mitchell. "Space" from *Me* by Inez Hogan, copyright 1954 by Inez Hogan.

GOLDEN GATE JUNIOR BOOKS, CALIFORNIA: *A Time for Flowers* by Mark Taylor, illustrated by Graham Booth. Text copyright 1967 by Mark Taylor; illustrations copyright 1967 by Graham Booth.

LOIS LENSKI: "Like Me" from *The Life I Live* by Lois Lenski, copyright 1965 by Lois Lenski. Published by Henry Z. Walck, Inc.

WILLIAM MORRIS AGENCY, INC.: Adaptation of *Tito's Hats* by Mel Ferrer, copyright © 1940 by Melchor G. Ferrer and Jean Charlotte.

HAROLD OBER ASSOCIATES INCORPORATED: "City" ("City: San Francisco") by Langston Hughes, from *The Langston Hughes Reader*, copyright © 1958 by Langston Hughes.

PARENTS' MAGAZINE ENTERPRISES, INC.: Adaptation of *Mabuna's Monkey* by James Rhodes from *Humpty Dumpty's Magazine*, May 1968, copyright 1968 Humpty Dumpty's Magazine.

THE VIKING PRESS, INC.: From *In My Mother's House* by Ann Nolan Clark, Illustrated by Velino Herrera, copyright 1941, copyright © renewed 1969 by Ann Nolan Clark.

PICTURE ACKNOWLEDGEMENTS: Photographs are from the sources listed below:
KEY: t, (top); m, (middle); b, (bottom); r, (right); l, (left)

Page 117 and 118, Harbrace; 119, Courtesy of the Field Museum of Natural History; 120 and 123, Harbrace; 127 and 128, The Bettmann Archive; 129-137, all Harbrace; 138 Courtesy of The Hallmark Gallery; 139 and 140, Harbrace; 193, (tl) Harbrace, (ml) Moore-McCormick Lines, (bl) Chesapeake & Ohio Railway, (tr) Harbrace, (br) Harbrace; 195 (l) Harbrace, (r) UPI; 197, Harbrace; 199, Texton's Bell Helicopter Co.; 200, Raimondo Borea; 201, United States Department of Agriculture; 203, Harbrace; 204, W. R. Wright; 205, Harbrace; 206, Coca-Cola; 207, Union Pacific Railroad; 208, (tl) Association of Railroads, (tr) W. R. Wright, (bl) Association of American Railroads, (br) W. R. Wright; 209, Seaboard Coastline Railroad; 210-213, Moore-McCormick Lines; 215, Harbrace; 216 and 217, UPI; 220, W. R. Wright; 222, (tr) Santa Fe Railroad, (bl) Harbrace, (br) Harbrace.
MINKUS PUBLICATIONS, INC.: *United States Stamp Album:* © 1968 by Minkus Publications, Inc. *The World Stamp Album:* © 1967 by Minkus Publications, Inc.

The artists in this book and the pages on which their work appears are as follows: Don Almquist pp. 7-57; Ted Lewin pp. 59, 60, 62, 65-111, 112, 113, 114, 124, 125, 142, 143, 145, 146, 188, 189, 190, 214, 222, 223, 224, 225, 228; Ray Ameijide pp. 147-187; Graham Booth pp. 230-253.

ISBN 0-15-332485-6

PUBLISHER'S NOTE: Evolution in this book is presented as a theory.

Contents

Different Faces, Different Places

Dragons, Giants, and Other Monsters

Collecting Things

Once Upon a Time

Going Places

A TIME FOR FLOWERS
by Mark Taylor

Different Faces, Different Places

The Painted House

The funny little smile on Father's face was something to see. He was having the best time ever, painting his house.

"Yes, that's what I'll paint next," he said to himself. "I'll paint a band of blue for the sky. Then I'll make big splashes of white for the clouds. Then maybe I'll paint silly pictures all over the house."

Before long Mother came into the yard.
How she laughed when she saw what Father
was doing.

"This will be an odd-looking house,"
Mother said. "But what a grand idea!"

Mother got some bright yellow paint.
She scrunched down on the ground and
began to paint flowers on the house.

Yes, Mother liked the idea of having
a house with funny pictures all over it.
But when the children came home from
school, well, that was something else.
They did not like the idea at all.

"What in the world!" cried Johnny when he saw the house. "All my friends will laugh at us. How could you do it, Father?"

"Now, children," said Father. "Wait until I tell you why I'm doing it."

"Yes, tell us," said Johnny's sister.

"Well," said Father, "in a way it is bad news. The city is growing so fast that they need our land. They are going to buy our lot, pull down the house, and build a bigger school. So you see, we have to move."

At first, no one said a word. Not one of the children liked the idea of moving. For one thing, they lived right next to the school, and so they were never late.

"Where are we going to move?" Danny asked his father.

"Maybe we can get a bigger house not too far away," Father answered. "I am trying to buy one with a big yard, too."

"Well, that's not bad news at all,"
said Mother. "It is about time we were
moving to a bigger house."

"I still don't get it," said little Jan.
"Why does our house have to be painted if
we have to move?"

"Just to have some fun," said Father.
"People always use plain colors on houses.
Well, I get tired of the same old thing,
and so, I'm doing something different.
Don't you want to help?"

"Yes!" the children cried. "May we paint any kind of picture we wish?"

"Yes, anything you wish," said Father. "But it does have to be different!"

Soon all the children were at work on the house. By sundown it was different from any other house in the country. It had pictures painted in many different colors by many different people.

It had apple trees with blue apples hiding in the leaves. It had green bears, red elephants, and a yellow hippopotamus. It had words and signs that little Jan had painted. And it had one tremendous black spider with pale green eyes.

Grandfather, who had come to help out, painted over all the windows. "I like to paint on glass," he said. "If it is dark inside, we can always put lights on. Anyway, the bulldozers will soon be pulling this old place down."

Days went by and no bulldozer came.
And no money was sent to Father for a
new house. And then, one day, he got
a letter in the mail.

As Father was reading the letter, his face turned pale. "Oh, no!" he cried as he fell into a chair. "I'm afraid we won't be moving. They are not going to buy our land after all. They now plan to build the school three blocks away."

"I was afraid of that," Grandmother said. "Things like that always happen."

But the children jumped up and down. They were glad they did not have to move.

And poor Father! It was a good thing he liked to paint, because now he had to paint the house over. And this time no one wanted to help. After all, what fun was it to paint a house plain white?

City

(To be read by the teacher)

In the morning the city
Spreads its wings
Making a song
In stone that sings.

In the evening the city
Goes to bed
Hanging lights
About its head.

LANGSTON HUGHES

The Lollipop Man

Glen Dee is a very small place. It has just two real streets. One street runs this way and the other one runs that way.

The shops and houses in Glen Dee are made of gray stone. One stone building is the Glen Dee school.

The school is at the crossing of the two streets. And the Lollipop Man is always at the crossing.

"Lollipop Man, please take us to the other side," cry the children.

Then the Lollipop Man puts his lollipop sign up high. And the children follow him to the other side.

"Thank you, Lollipop Man!" the children sing out.

And the old man, with a smile on his face, answers, "Thank **you**, my friends."

Rain or shine, the Lollipop Man is always at the school crossing to help the children.

But one day, not so long ago, it looked as if this would be the last time for the Lollipop Man to help the children cross the street. On that day, the Lollipop Man looked sad as he held his sign up high.

"Children, this is my last day," he said with a sigh. "But I won't forget you. And I hope you won't forget me. Maybe someday I'll come back and play my bagpipes for you."

The children wondered why the old man was leaving his job. That night Janet asked her father about her old friend.

"This was his last day, Janet," said her father. "The Lollipop Man is now too old to work. And our policeman in Glen Dee has no work to do. From now on, he will take the place of the Lollipop Man."

Janet did not like this idea one bit. She tried not to think about it, but it was hard to think about anything else.

The next morning,
cold rain was falling
as the children came
to school.

"Get moving, get
moving," the policeman
said as he held up the
round sign.

"Thank you, thank you,
Mr. Lollipop Policeman,"
said Janet as she got
to the other side.

But the policeman just sighed and said,
"What a silly thing for me to be doing!"

At noon the policeman went home for
lunch. After lunch, he sat by the fire
and went to sleep. He was still sleeping
when the children came back from lunch.

The children waited at the crossing
until no cars were in sight. Then they
crossed the street and ran to the school.

Later that afternoon when school let out, the policeman was still not at the crossing. But now the children were afraid to cross the street. And what a sight they saw!

One of the streets was filled with sheep. Some of the sheep were looking in shop windows. Three sheep had walked right into a food shop.

The other street was lined with cars and trucks, honking, honking, honking. With all that honking, the sheep were soon running wild.

All the people in Glen Dee came down
to the crossing to see what was going on.
All, that is, but the sleepy policeman.
He was still sleeping by his fire.

"Where did all the cars come from?"
asked Janet's father.

"The big road is blocked off," yelled
the red-faced driver of a delivery truck.
"We had to come this way, and now we are
stuck. Don't you have a policeman?"

"We have something better!" cried Janet.
"Look, he is coming now!"

Down the street came the
Lollipop Man, all dressed up.
He was playing his bagpipes.

The cars stopped honking.
The sheep stopped running wild.
And bit by bit, still playing
his bagpipes, the Lollipop Man
got the cars moving.

"Well!" cried Janet's father.
"We may not need a policeman
in Glen Dee. But we do need
the Lollipop Man!"

"We do!" said all the others.
"We will let the Lollipop Man
stay as long as he wants!"

And they all followed him and
his bagpipes down the street.

Mabuna's Little Pet

Mabuna was a small boy who lived in a village. The village was not far from the jungle. All the other children in the village had pets. But Mabuna had no pet at all.

"What kind of pet would you like?" his father asked him one day.

"A pet monkey!" Mabuna cried. "That is what I want."

23

So one day Mabuna's father gave him a little monkey. The monkey chattered and tried to bite Mabuna's father. But when Mabuna held him, the monkey did not bite.

The pet monkey was always getting into things. He took bananas from a dish. Then he chattered and ran up a tall tree to eat the bananas. He pulled the tails of the dogs, too. And he turned over baskets in the house.

"Mabuna," his mother said one night, "we will have to do something about your little monkey."

"But he is my friend!" cried Mabuna. "If I keep an eye on him, may I keep him?"

"We will see," said Mabuna's father.

But Mabuna's pet
kept getting into
more and more things.
One day he put all
the sticks of dry
wood on the fire at
one time. Mabuna's
mother cried for help
when she saw what the monkey did.
But it was too late. She had no
wood for cooking that night.

"That monkey can't stay," she said.
"Look at the hard work he makes for me."

Mabuna tried to hold onto his pet.
But his father took the monkey and walked
off into the jungle. He came back alone.

That night, Mabuna could not eat.
He went to bed and looked out at the
big yellow moon in the blue-black sky.
He kept thinking about his little pet,
alone out in the jungle.

When his father and mother were sleeping,
Mabuna got up. Without making a sound,
he was out of the house. He ran from the
village, down the path, and into the jungle.

How different the jungle looked at night!
How different the jungle sounded. Mabuna
went on and on, crawling under vines and
jumping over logs. Where was his pet?

By now, Mabuna was far from the village.
He was alone and lost. Away in the dark
night, animals cried out. Wild birds made
wild sounds.

Mabuna was hungry and frightened.
But most of all he missed his little pet.
He sat under a tree and wanted to cry —
but he did not. Soon he went to sleep.

He woke up when something took hold of his hand. It was now morning, and the sun was shining.

Mabuna jumped to his feet. Right before him, chattering away, was his pet monkey!

"Where were you?" asked Mabuna. "I looked for you most of the night, and now I am lost. Can you show me how to get back to the village?"

The monkey ran in front of Mabuna, and then he turned to see if the boy was following. Mabuna followed his pet, and in time they came to the village path.

Most of the village men were out in the
jungle looking for Mabuna. His mother
came running to him as he came down the
path. She was so happy to have him back
that she did not scold him. Then Mabuna
told her how his pet monkey had helped
him get out of the jungle.

When Mabuna's father came back, he
scolded a little. "I have told you and
told you not to go into the jungle alone,"
he said. "But I am glad that your little
pet could bring you home."

"Then I may keep him?" Mabuna asked.

"Yes," said the father. "But you
must look after him and teach him."

"I will," cried Mabuna.

Tito's Hats

A boy named Tito lived in a house high in
the mountains of Mexico. He lived with
his father, his grandmother, and his
little sister.

Tito had a hat that was very old.
One day when he was on the side of the
mountain, a wind came up. It took Tito's
hat right off his head. Tito had no way
of getting his hat because it rolled over
and over down the side of the mountain.

That night Tito told his father about
the hat.

"I'll take you to town tomorrow to buy
you a new hat," his father said.

So Tito went to sleep thinking of new
hats and the kind he would like to get.

The next morning before the sun was up,
Tito and his father set out.

Many people were on the road to town.
They were all going to market. When the
sun came up, Tito and his father could
see the town in front of them.

When they came to the market, it was
filled with people. Men were shouting
and talking and buying all kinds of things.

Each time they went
by a different hat shop,
Tito tried on the hats.
But not one of them was
the right size. Some
were too big and others
were too small.

Then, as they came from the
last shop, so many people were
in the market place that Tito
lost his father. Tito looked
and looked for his father, but
he was not to be found. All the
faces Tito saw were new to him.

Tito went all over the market
place looking for his father.
At last he saw an old man who
was sitting by a long pole with
many hats on it. At the top
of the pole was the finest hat
that Tito had ever seen.

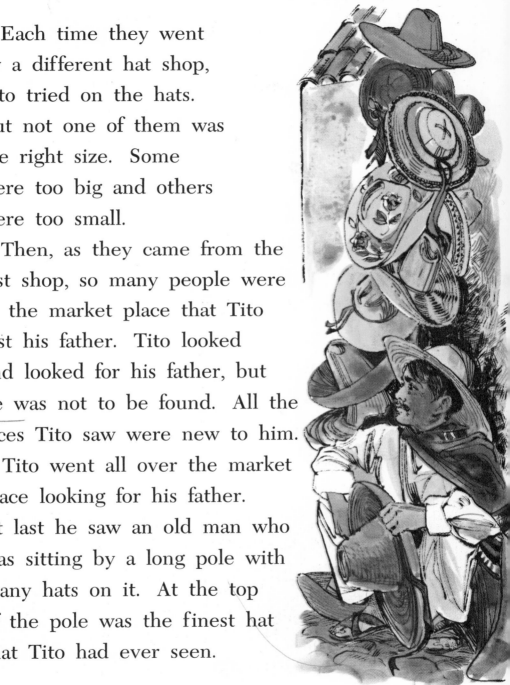

The old man took the hat from the pole.
But when Tito tried on the hat, it was
just the smallest bit too small.

As Tito was looking at the hat, his
father walked up. Tito showed his father
the hat. His father smiled, and so did
the old man. But when Tito tried on the
hat for his father, they all saw that it
was just the smallest bit too small.

Without saying a word, Tito's father
gave back the hat. Then he took hold
of Tito's hand and walked away.

They went from the market place and
walked up a narrow street.

At the end of the long, narrow street, they came to a wide one. They walked up the wide street until they came to a very different kind of shop.

They went into a room that opened right onto the street. In the room a big man was standing in back of a white chair.

"But I don't want my hair cut," Tito said.

"You have needed a haircut for a long, long time," said Tito's father. "Now get up into the chair."

Tito did as his father told him to do. He got into the chair and sat very still.

Bit by bit, the man cut Tito's hair. It seemed to Tito that the man was taking the longest time ever for a haircut.

After it was over, Tito got down from the chair. How different his head felt!

Then his father gave the man some money,
and they went off. They went back down the
wide street, back down the narrow street,
and back into the market. They went right
to the old man who had the hats.

The old man took the same hat that
Tito had tried on before. Now it was just
the right size! Tito was the proudest boy
in town.

How Tito laughed! "So that is why I
had to have my hair cut," he said.

Five Fish for Supper

Part 1

The bright sun was on the sea and on
the sand. The sand was hot on children's
feet. They had to run fast, in big hops,
to get over the hot sand and down to the
cool, cool water.

Some of the big children swam out where
the sea was deep. But Tonio, like other
children his age, was still too little to
go out in deep water by himself.

Tonio was playing in the place he liked
most of all. He was in the tide pool.

Tonio liked to look into the water at
the tide pool to see the small sea animals
that hid under the rocks. He liked to drop
small stones into the pool and see the
little animals moving away from danger.

From the tide pool, Tonio could look
back over the sand and see his mother.
And she could see him.

Tonio's mother, dressed all in black, sat out in front of a small white house. Her chair was on the sand, and all around her was a fish net. She was working on the net, pulling it together so it would hold the fish.

She put down the net and looked out at the water. The boats were coming in.

"Tonio! Tonio!" she called to her son. The boy came running from the tide pool.

"Run down to the boats," the mother said. "Get five fish for supper. And don't forget they must be fresh. Take this money."

Tonio picked up his little pail. Then, with the money in one hand and the pail in the other, he was off on a run.

As Tonio ran, he began thinking about his father. He used to bring home all the fish they could eat. But one day he went out too far in his small boat. A big wind came up, and Tonio's father never came back.

From then on, things were different in Tonio's home. His mother worked day and night on the nets. His older brothers moved to the big city to look for work. Tonio and his smaller brothers and sister stayed in the fishing village by the sea. But they, too, did what they could to help.

Tonio filled his pail with sea water. He had come to the place where the men had pulled their boats up onto the sand. In their boats were boxes and boxes of fish still wet from the sea.

Tonio always felt a little sad when he saw boxes of fish. They looked like the ones his father used to bring home.

"Please, my mother wants five fish for supper," Tonio said. He gave the money to a man, who began picking out the fish.

"One, two, three, four, five!" said the man. "There you are, Tonio, five fine fish for your supper."

"Are they fresh?" Tonio asked. "My mother said that they must be fresh."

"What do you mean?" the man laughed. "They are so fresh they will take to the sea if you don't keep an eye on them."

Tonio thanked the man and ran off, over the hot sand. Water that splashed from the pail felt good on Tonio's legs.

Part 2

A Fish That Was Too Fresh

When Tonio came to the tide pool, he
sat on a rock to rest. As he rested, he
put his hand into the pail. A big, shiny
fish under his hand felt as cool as the
sea water.

"I wonder how a big, shiny fish like
this would look in my pool," he said.
Then he jumped and slid off the rock.
For the big shiny fish was moving!
It was not dead!

40

In a flash, Tonio picked up the shiny
fish and slid it into the tide pool.
At first the fish did not move at all.
Was it dead?

Then as Tonio looked at it, the shiny
fish swam to the far end of the pool.
Then it swam from one side to the other.
And at last it hid where the rocks made
dark shadows on the water.

The boy picked up his pail and ran
for home.

"What am I going to tell my mother?"
he wondered as he ran.

When Tonio got home, he gave his mother
the pail. "One, two, three, four — FOUR!"
said his mother. "Tonio, there are just
four fish. Did you not ask for five?"

"Yes, I asked for five," said Tonio.

"Then go back, right now," said his
mother. "Tell the man that when you ask
for five fish, you mean five. Five means
five, not four! Go back and get the other
fish. And get a fresh one!"

Tonio ran. As he ran by the tide pool,
he felt the eyes of the shiny fish looking
up at him from the shadows. "I hope I
don't have to take him," he sighed.

The man was cleaning out the boat when
Tonio got there.

"My mother wants the other fish," he
said. "We need five fish for supper."

"But I gave you five," said the man.
"Five fine fish, the freshest ones I had."

"Yes, but one was too fresh," said
Tonio. "It was not yet dead, and so I
put it into the tide pool. It looked so
happy there in the water I could not take
it out. Won't you please let me have
another fish? I have no money to buy
it with, but I'll work for you."

"I would be glad to let you have one more fish," said the man. "But I just sold my last ones."

"Then where can I get one?" Tonio asked.

"I don't think you can," said the man. "Not now. Any fish that came in were sold long ago. Most of them were loaded onto trucks that will take them to the city."

"Then what can I do?" asked Tonio.

"I'll tell you," said the man. He was a kind man who had six children of his own. "You must go home and tell your mother," he said to Tonio. "Tell her what you did with the fish that was too fresh."

This was a hard thing for Tonio to do, but he did it.

At first Tonio's mother scolded her
son for not telling all that had happened.
She scolded him, too, for leaving one
of the fish in the tide pool.

"I can go without fish for supper,"
Tonio said. "But I'll try to get the
fish from the tide pool if I must."

"No, my little one," said his mother.
"You won't have to get the shiny fish
this time. But the next time you must
bring home all the fish you pay for."

And that same night, long after supper,
the high tide came in. It came over the
rocks and filled the tide pool until it
ran over. Then the big, shiny fish swam
out of the pool and far out to sea.

Home

This is my Mother's house;
My Father made it.
He made it with adobe bricks;
He made it strong;
He made it big;
He made it high;
My Mother's house,
I live in it.

This is my Mother's house;
My Mother plastered it
With brown clay;
On the outside
My Mother plastered it.

The inside walls are white;
My Mother made them white;
The floor is smooth;
My Mother made it smooth,
For me to live there. . . .

47

In my Mother's house
All day
I play and work;
All night
I sleep.

The walls come close around me
In a good way.
I can see them;
I can feel them;
I live with them.

This house is good to me,
It keeps me;
I like it,
My Mother's house.

My Mother's house,
It does not stand alone.
Its sister houses are around it;
Its sister houses are close to it.

Like holding hands,
The houses stand close together
Around the plaza.

Houses are the stay-in places,
But the plaza
Is the live-in place
For all the people.
In the plaza the people work;
In the plaza the people play
And sing and dance

And make ready for feasting.
It is the place
For all the people.

The plaza keeps the people together,
And the houses
With their backs to the mountains,
Stand facing the plaza
And shut it in.

My Mother's house,
It does not stand alone;
Its sister houses
Are all around it.

We are the people
Living together,
All of us together.

We live here
In the houses,
In the plaza
Together.

A Joke on Eagle Feather

Eagle Feather was singing as he drove
the sheep and goats down the mountain.
He was glad the sun was setting and it
was time to go home.

Each morning he took the sheep and
goats to the high hills. He took them
where they could get good grass and leaves
to eat. He kept them from getting lost.

He worked hard to look after them
because each morning his mother said,
"Look after the sheep and goats, my son,
like a good Navajo."

Eagle Feather was a Navajo Indian.
His skin was brown, and his hair was long
and black. He had a red band around his
head to keep the hair out of his eyes.
He was tall and strong, and he could run
like the wind.

"Hi!" he said to the sheep and goats.
He ran after them to make them go faster.

Down the mountain he could see his
little brother and sister. Their names
were Teasing Boy and Morning Bird. They
were waiting for him by the corral.

"Open the gate!" he called.

They opened the gate. He drove the
sheep and goats into the corral, and
they were safe for the night.

Teasing Boy was jumping about like a goat. He was glad to see his brother, but he liked to tease him, too. "A man came here when you were away," he said.

"What man?" asked Eagle Feather.

"A big man," said Teasing Boy. "He came on that big yellow horse. He talked to Mother. I think he wants you to go away with him."

Eagle Feather asked his sister, "Did a man come here?"

"Yes," said Morning Bird.

"I won't go away with him," said Eagle Feather. "I like my home."

Teasing Boy and Morning Bird looked
at each other. They put their hands over
their mouths to keep from laughing.

"He can't make me go away," said
Eagle Feather.

"The man is here now," said Teasing Boy.

Eagle Feather looked at the hogan, the
house where they lived. It was a small
house with just one room. From the outside
it looked like a little round hill.

"I'm not going in there," Eagle Feather
said. "I don't want to see that man."

"He won't hurt you," said Morning Bird.
"Mother wants you to see him."

Mother came to the door of the hogan.
She had on the green jacket and long,
brown skirt that Eagle Feather liked so
well. He liked to feel the jacket, for
it was as soft as fur. Around her skirt
were bright bands of yellow and red.

"Come!" she called. "Supper is ready."
Teasing Boy and Morning Bird took hold
of Eagle Feather. He let them pull him
into the hogan.

There was a fire on the floor of the
hogan. There were stones around the fire.
The smoke went out of the top of the hogan.

A man was sitting by the fire.

Eagle Feather stopped when he saw the
man. "Father!" he said.

Teasing Boy and Morning Bird were
laughing. "We played a joke on our
brother," said Teasing Boy. "We told
him a man was here. We did not say
who it was."

Father had been away a day and a night. He had been away to trade one of his old horses for a better one.

Eagle Feather sat down by him. "Did you trade the horse?"

"Yes," said Father. "Now I have a good yellow horse. He is out under the trees."

"They told me a man was here and he wanted to take me away," said Eagle Feather. "Then I did not want to come in."

"You don't want to go away?" asked Father.

"No," said Eagle Feather. "I want to stay here. I want to look after the sheep and goats and ride the horses."

"Don't you want to go with me to the trading post tomorrow?" asked Father.

"Yes!" said Eagle Feather. "I want to go to the trading post. Is that what my brother and sister were teasing me about?"

"Yes," said Father with a smile. "Tomorrow we will go to the trading post."

Like Me

(To be read by the teacher)

All around the world
there are children like me.
In many strange places
they happen to be.
They eat and they sleep,
they run and they play;
They work and are helpful
day by day.
Their dress and their food
may seem very queer,
Their homes too are different
from those I know here.
But all round the world
they are still just like me,
In living and giving,
good friends are we.

LOIS LENSKI

Can You Read This?

At one time in this country, a man had to do most things for himself. He had to grow his own food or look for things to eat. He had to build his own house. He had to make things to protect himself from cold winds and the hot sun. A man had very little money to get things he needed.

But there were still things people could not make. Some people could not make tools they needed. Then they would trade. A man who could not make tools might have more flour than he needed. He could look for a man who made tools. He could trade his flour for tools.

When people needed things, they sometimes traded their time and work for

60

them. A man who was good at farm work would trade his work for a horse he needed. In this way, people helped each other.

People began to live close together. Now there were more people to trade with each other. A man might make a living making tools or building houses. He did not have to grow his own food.

More money came into use. With money, people got paid for their work and for the things they made. With money, they could buy the things they wanted. They could pay people to work for them. There was no need to trade things. It was good to have money.

---

1. What is this selection about?
   How people got things they needed.
   How people lived in early days.
   How people planted seeds.
2. Why was it good to have money?

When You Read

(To be read with the teacher)

Words That Have the Same Sounds but Different Meanings

Can you tell the <u>flour</u> from the <u>flower</u>?
How are the two underlined words the
same? Are they spelled the same way? Do
they have the same meaning?

Can you tell which of these pictures
is the <u>sun</u>? which one <u>is the son</u>?

Some words sound the same, but do
not mean the same thing. The way these
words are used in sentences helps you know
what they mean.

Try This

Read each sentence. Find the words that sound the same but do not mean the same thing.

1. I can't see because I have something in my eye.
2. The boy was pale when he handed his mother the pail of fish.
3. Tonio's mother could see just four fish in the pail of sea water.
4. We read a story about a boy with a red wagon.
5. Where would you see a horse made of wood?

What two words in the first sentence sound the same? How are they spelled?

What two words in each of the other sentences sound the same? How are they spelled?

How do you know what the words mean?

Words That Have the Same Spellings but Different Sounds

Read these sentences.

I <u>live</u> on Market Street.

You can buy <u>live</u> fish at the market.

Read the first sentence. Is the vowel sound in <u>live</u> a short vowel sound or a long vowel sound? How do you know?

Read the second sentence. Is the vowel sound in <u>live</u> a short vowel sound or a long vowel sound? How do you know?

Some words are spelled the same but do not sound the same. The other words in a sentence help you say them.

Try This

Read these sentences.

1. You can <u>read</u> the story I just <u>read</u>.
2. Who can <u>lead</u> Ben to the <u>lead</u> pencils?

64

Dragons, Giants, and Other Monsters

In the World of Make-Believe

When you were very little, did you ever
wonder if dragons and giants were real?

For many years people have told stories
about dragons, giants, and other monsters.
We do not know who made up the first story
about a monster. But we do know that
stories about monsters never grow old.
Children today enjoy them the same as
children did long ago.

We know that monsters, like dragons and
giants, are not real. Yet there was a
time, long ago, when some people believed
in many different kinds of monsters.

Long ago people believed that monsters
lived in the sea, in the high mountains,
in dark caves, and in the deep forest.
Maybe people believed in monsters because
they knew so little about their world.

Some of the monsters that people
believed in were very big, like giants
and dragons. Others, they said, were
no bigger than a cat. They believed
that all monsters, big or small, could
do things that real people or animals
could not do.

Many of the monsters in old stories looked like mixed-up animals. Some were parts of two different kinds of animals put together. Other monsters were part man and part animal. Still others were giant men. Sometimes the giants had more than one head.

In old pictures, this monster looks like a lion with a man's head. It has red eyes, many teeth, and long hair on its face. It has a long tail with a sting on the end. People said this mixed-up animal could make soft and happy sounds.

This monster is part bird and part snake. Its head, legs, and wings look like a rooster's. The rest of the monster looks like a snake. People believed the monster could cut open rocks, set fire to trees, and kill people.

This monster is part lion and part bird. Its head is like an eagle's. People believed this monster was brave and good. They said it made big nests of real gold.

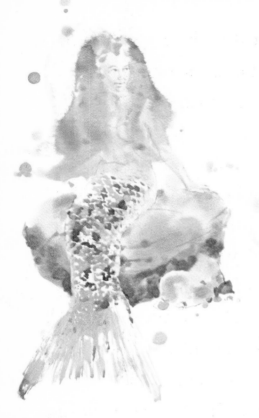

This monster lives
in the sea, but she
sometimes comes out
of the water and sits
on rocks. Her face is
white, her eyes are
blue, and her hair
is long and green.
Many people say
she likes to sing
in the moonlight.

This monster is
called the Mushrush.
The Mushrush has two
legs like a bird's
and two legs like a
cat's. Its head is
a bit like a man's.
But it has horns and
long hair.

70

No one ever saw a Mushrush, or a dragon, or any other monster. The monsters in stories are just made-up animals or people. They are not real. They never lived.

In some monster stories, the monster is so mean that it has to be killed. Many stories tell how a brave knight, or other brave man, found a way to kill it. In other stories, the job of killing the monster falls to a boy or girl. Children sometimes do what brave knights cannot do.

Not all monsters in stories are mean. There are good giants and dragons as well as bad ones. But monsters do not frighten us today because we know they are not real.

Olaf and the Dragon

Many years ago, in an old castle, there lived two brave knights. They were named Sir Charles and Sir Egbert. With the two knights lived Olaf, the page boy.

Sir Charles and Sir Egbert had fine times riding horses and being brave. Olaf ran after birds with his little red flag. Their castle was not big and grand. Yet, they were happy — but for one thing.

Not far from the castle, deep in the dark forest, lived a terrible dragon. He frightened the children and spread fear over all the land. At night his terrible roar made the children cry and kept the older people from sleeping.

One morning, after a very roaring night, Sir Charles said, "This has to stop! Are we not the bravest knights for miles around?"

"Yes, we are," said Sir Egbert. "There are no other knights in the country, and so we are the bravest ones."

"So," said Sir Charles, "it is very clear what we must do. It is up to us to kill the roaring dragon!"

"Oh my!" said Sir Egbert.

"Oh dear!" said Olaf.

Sir Charles went over to the window and looked out at the forest. He was thinking.

"I know how to do it," he said.
"But first we must see the wizard."

Olaf got the horses, and off they
went to see the wizard.

"Change us into dragons!" said the
knights when they met the wizard.

The wizard looked at them in surprise.

"Why dragons?" he asked.

"To kill a dragon," said Sir Charles.

"You must know that it takes a dragon
to kill a dragon," said Sir Egbert.

The wizard began to shake his head.
"I can change you into dragons, all right,"
he said. "But it may not be the best way."

But the two knights kept on asking.
So the wizard opened a box where he kept
his wizard things. He felt around for
a small bottle. At last he found it.

"This is magic stuff," he said. "Take
a little of this at bedtime, and in the
morning you will be dragons."

74

The three thanked the wizard. As they
were leaving, the wizard said something
to Olaf that the others could not hear.
He told Olaf to face the dragon as a man.

Olaf smiled and waved good-bye with
his little red flag. Then, holding the
bottle of magic so it would not spill,
the three rode back to the castle.

75

That night, after Olaf went to sleep,
Sir Charles opened the bottle. He and
Sir Egbert each took a bit of the stuff.

Then, leaving Olaf in the castle, the
two knights rode off into the forest.

All night they waited. In the morning
they were dragons! They knew what they
had to do.

The two knights, who were now dragons,
found the roaring dragon in his cave.
After a terrible fight, the roaring dragon
fell down — dead!

Poor Olaf! When he woke up, he was all alone. He knew what had happened, but he did not know what to do about it.

Then he saw the bottle, and he picked it up. Some of the magic stuff was still in the bottom.

"If I drink it," he said to himself, "I, too, will change into a dragon. But that would just make another dragon."

And then the wizard's words came back to him.

YOU MUST FACE THE DRAGON AS A MAN.

Olaf put the bottle into his pocket
and set out for the forest. He tried
to be brave.

He looked on one side of the forest,
and he looked on the other side of the
forest. He looked at the top of the hill,
and he looked at the bottom of the hill.

At last, near the mouth of a dark cave,
he found the two dragons. They were asleep.
Olaf wanted to run away, but he did not.
He knew he had to change the dragons back
to men. And so, he went nearer and nearer
and nearer.

When he was very close, he took the
bottle from his pocket and let a drop or
two fall on each of the dragons.

Then he ran!

When Olaf came to the end of the forest,
he was so tired he could not run any more.
He fell down on the grass, and soon he
was fast asleep.

Some time later, after the magic drops
had worked their magic, Sir Charles and
Sir Egbert came out of the forest as men.
They found Olaf still asleep in the grass.
They picked him up and took him, still
sleeping, back to the castle.

The news spread fast that the dragon
had been killed. When the king learned
about Olaf and how he had helped, he
called for a holiday. He called for the
holiday so he could thank the boy for
being so brave.

Now in the forest there are no more dragons. And in the castle live three brave knights. They are Sir Charles, Sir Egbert, and Sir Olaf!

Sir Charles and Sir Egbert have fine days riding their horses and being brave. Sir Olaf runs after birds, waving his little red flag.

Their castle is not big and grand, but they are all very happy.

Real Monsters

For years and years, people of many
lands have told stories about dragons.
They have painted many pictures of them.
They have put dragons on flags and kites.
They have made dragons out of rock, clay,
and wood. They have made masks shaped
like a dragon's head.

Did the people of long ago ever see
real dragons? Did real dragons ever live?
Do dragons live today? What do you think?

Does the picture on this page make you
think of dragons? The picture shows real
animals that lived millions of years ago.
But the animals are dinosaurs, not dragons.

Some dinosaurs looked a little like dragons. Some had long teeth and long claws. Others had wings and could fly.

But we know dinosaurs were not dragons. For one thing, almost all dragon stories have people in them. But dinosaurs lived millions of years ago, long before there were people in the world. Also, dragons are pictured with fire or smoke coming from their mouths. Yet no living animal, then or now, could make fire or smoke.

So the dragons in books and pictures are not dinosaurs.

Another animal that looks a little
like a dragon is living today. It is
a kind of lizard. It is called a dragon
lizard, or just plain dragon.

We know about dragon lizards for they
have lived in some of our big city zoos.
They are the biggest lizards in the world
today. Some even grow to be 12 feet long.

The dragon lizard has a long, bright yellow tongue. As the lizard sniffs around for food, its tongue flashes in and out, like a tongue of fire.

When the animal's big red mouth is open wide, it shows rows of long teeth. They look almost like the teeth on a saw.

A dragon lizard must hunt for its food. It hunts and eats other wild animals. Because of its strong jaws, this lizard can eat even the skin and bones of other animals. When it is hungry, it eats and eats all it can hold. Then it may sit around for days and not eat at all.

At night a dragon lizard hides in its cave. The cave is one that the lizard has dug out with its strong claws.

Some people believe this lizard is a real dragon. They believe the dragon's fire is the lizard's yellow tongue and its red mouth. Do you believe it, too?

A Giant of the Sea

What is the biggest animal in the
world today? It is not the elephant.

What is the biggest animal that has
ever lived? It is not the dinosaur.

The blue whales are the biggest
animals that ever lived, and they are
still living today. Of all the animals,
they are the real giants. They are giants
that live in the sea.

There are different kinds of whales.
They are all big animals, and they all
live in the sea. They look like fish,
but they are not fish. They are mammals,
the same as cats, dogs, and elephants.

When you think of a mammal, you think
of an animal with hair. Even an elephant
has hair when it is a baby.

At one time, whales also had hair.
Now all they have is just a bit of hair
on chin and head.

Millions of years ago, whales lived on land. They had two pairs of legs for walking and running.

Over the years, the land changed, and the seas changed. And the whales changed, too, and they began to live in the sea. This happened so very long ago that we don't know when or why the whale changed from a land animal to a sea animal.

In time, the whale lost its pair of back legs. The two front legs changed. The front legs now help the whale to swim, but not to walk.

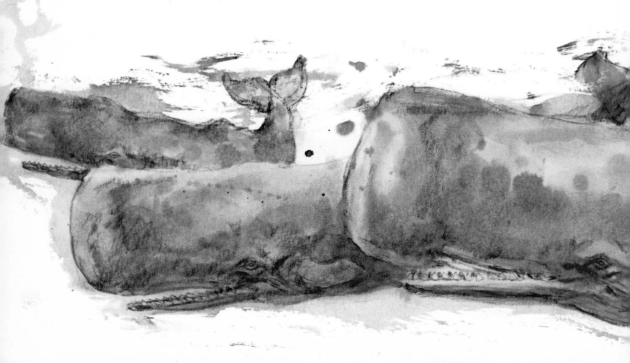

The whale changed, and it now swims like a fish and looks like a fish. But it is still a mammal.

Like all living things, whales need air. A fish needs air, too. But a fish can take air right from the water. It never needs to come to the top for air.

A whale can't take air from the water. When it needs air, it must swim to the top to get it. Don't forget, whales are mammals. Whales take in air like other mammals.

A mother whale has one baby at a time. A baby whale is called a calf.

A new blue whale calf is about three times as big as a big elephant. But even a baby that big stays near its mother to get the care it needs.

The calf gets milk from the mother whale. Whale milk is very rich. The rich whale milk helps the calf to grow fast.

A whale is a good mother. She takes good care of her giant baby.

For many years, men have hunted and killed whales. Because of this, giant blue whales are now rare animals.

It is sad to think that someday all blue whales may be killed, or die off. But that is what may happen if men do not do more to protect the rare animals.

In the years to come, there may be no blue whales at all. Then what will be the biggest animal in the world?

The Whale

If you ever ever ever ever ever
   If you ever ever ever meet a whale.
You must never never never never never
   You must never never never touch its tail:
For if you ever ever ever ever ever
   If you ever ever ever touch its tail,
You will never never never never never
   You will never never meet another whale.

TRADITIONAL

Jack the Giant Killer

At Land's End, a man and his son had
a small farm. The son was a good boy,
and very bright. His name was Jack.

But for one thing, Jack and his father
would have been happy together on the farm.
They lived in fear of a terrible giant.

The giant lived in a cave in the hills. When he got hungry, he would come down from the hills at night and hunt for something to eat.

Many a good cow, and many a fine calf, and many a brave man did the giant take. Yes, many did he take, when he came down to Land's End in the dark of night.

One morning, Jack's father said, "Will no one go after this giant and kill him? Are there no brave sons in Land's End?"

"Father, I am brave," said Jack. "I will go and kill the giant."

Jack got a spade, a horn, and an ax.
As soon as it was almost dark, he set
out for the hill where the giant lived.

With the spade, he dug a deep, wide
pit at the mouth of the giant's cave.
He found some sticks and placed them
over the pit. Then he put grass over
the sticks. No one would ever know
there was a pit under the grass.

After that, Jack sat down on the far
side of the pit. He got out his horn
and blew a tremendous blast on it.
He blew blast after blast on his horn.

The giant came to the door of his cave. "How dare you!" he roared. "How dare you blow that horn when I am sound asleep! I'll get you for that! I will eat you up, right down to your last bone!"

Jack did not move from his place on the other side of the pit. "Come and get me, if you dare!" he called to the giant. "I'm not afraid of you. I have known many a giant bigger than you."

With a terrible roar, the giant came from his cave. Still roaring and with a tremendous crash, he smashed into the pit.

Jack jumped to his feet in a flash.
He ran to the pit, hit the giant over
the head with his ax, and killed him.
Then he picked up his spade and filled
in the pit.

After that, Jack made his way into
the giant's cave. He was overjoyed to
see many bags of gold. For the giant was
not just a terrible giant who ate people
and animals. The giant was also a robber.

Jack ran home and told his father what
had happened. Soon a crowd of people came
to hear his story. They were overjoyed
to hear that the giant was dead.

"We must allow Jack to keep the gold
the giant had in his cave," said a man.

"Yes, yes," said all the people who
crowded around Jack. "We will allow him
to keep the money, for he has made this
land safe at last. And from now on, he
will be called Jack the Giant Killer."

To this very day, he is still known as
Jack the Giant Killer.

The Horrible, Terrible Giant

The king was sad. The king's children were sad. The king's wife, who was the queen, was sad. So were all the other people of the land.

A horrible, terrible giant had moved into the forest. He was now living just under the city wall.

At night, the horrible, terrible giant
made horrible, terrible sounds. People
for miles and miles around could hear them.

The king would crawl down to the foot
of his bed under the clean, white sheets.
His wife, who was the queen, would get up
and walk the floor. The children would
stand by the castle windows with their
hands over their ears, biting their lips.

Some nights the giant's sounds were
so terrible that the windows and doors
shook all night. It was a wonder that
the castle itself did not fall down.

One morning the king and queen were sitting in the kitchen of the castle.

"Drink your milk. It is good for you," said the queen. "And eat your eggs."

"I'm too sleepy," said the king, putting his hand under his chin. "That horrible, terrible giant roared all night long."

"He always roars at night," said the queen. "I think he must be hungry."

"Oh, dear!" cried the king, rubbing his jaws. "Is that why he roars all the time?"

"It may be," snapped his wife. "You will have to find out."

"But how?" asked the king, turning pale. "I can't very well go out and ask him, can I? That would scare me no end. There must be some other way to find out."

The king stood on his head. He always stood on his head when he had some big thinking to do. He could think better standing on his head than on his feet.

"I have it!" cried the king, jumping
to his feet. "I should look up the word
GIANTS in one of my books."

The king went to his big book room,
which he called his study. He looked
in book after book. At last he found
a book which had this name.

WHAT A KING NEEDS TO KNOW

ABOUT GIANTS

He sat down at his desk and called
his wife. Then he began to read.

Giants roar when they are hungry.
They should then be fed. Most giants
eat cows, sheep, goats, and pigs.
Here is what other giants eat.

candy and cake   **raisins and grapes**
peanut butter   **apples and bananas**

But horrible, terrible giants eat
little girls with long yellow hair.

"Well, that's that! It is clear what we
should do," said the king. "I'll make a
lunch box and you find the girl for it."

The queen went out to find the girl.
The king got some boards and went to work
with his hammer and nails. When the last
board was nailed, he put this sign on top.

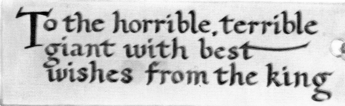

To the horrible, terrible
giant with best
wishes from the king

The Girl with Yellow Hair

The king looked up as the queen came
in with the yellow-haired girl.

"Good afternoon," he said to the girl.
"I think we have met before."

"Yes, Father, we have!" cried the girl.
"And I am not going to be fed to that
horrible, terrible giant! And you're
not going to put me into that lunch box.
If you try to put me into it, I'll make
some horrible, terrible sounds myself!"

At that, the king stood on his head.
"Was there no other yellow-haired girl?"
he asked his wife.

"Not one that I could get," said the
queen. "They're all too scared of me.
They run and hide when they see me coming."

The king jumped to his feet.

"Did you get an idea?" cried the queen.

The king shook his head. "No, I didn't,"
he said. "I'm going to get my thinking
cap. That should help me know what to do."

The mother and girl stood face to face
in the room. "Sometimes your father isn't
very bright," sighed the king's wife.

"Then I'll go and have a talk with the
giant," said the girl. "I'm not scared."

"You don't dare!" said the queen.
"What if the giant won't let you talk?
What if he's hungry and eats you first?"

"I don't care if he's hungry or not,"
said the girl, waving good-bye.

She went out the gate, over the brick
wall, and into the tall green forest.
At last, when the afternoon was about over,
she met the horrible, terrible giant.

"Hi," said the girl to the giant.
"I think it's time we had a little talk!"

The giant looked down at the girl.
"What's there to talk about?" he asked.

"Your terrible, horrible sounds, for
one thing," she said. "If you don't stop
all that roaring, I'm going to spank you!"

"I'm hungry!" said the giant.

"Then what about all that shaking?"

"It gets cold out here in the woods,"
said the giant. "I shake when I'm cold.
I do wish people didn't hate me so."

"They hate you for eating girls with
long yellow hair!" cried the girl.

"I?" said the giant. "Don't be silly!
Why, I never ate a girl—or a boy or a
man or a woman. Look at me. I have just
one tooth, so how could I eat people?
I like people—but not to eat!"

And the horrible, terrible giant
began to cry horrible, terrible tears.

"Now, now," said the girl. "I didn't
mean to hurt your feelings. Do dry your
tears. You can live in our castle and be
my friend. You can have all you can eat."

"Soft things?" asked the giant.

"Yes, soft things," said the girl.
"Things you don't have to bite or chew.
But you must promise, no more shaking.
And no more horrible, terrible sounds."

"I promise," said the giant, smiling.
And when he smiled his big smile, he did
not look horrible or terrible at all.

A Monster of Your Own

How would you like to make a monster of your own? It isn't a hard thing to do.

First, think of the different kinds of animals. Think of those that live on land. Think of those that fly in the air. Think of those that swim in the sea or in a wide river.

Next, think of the animal parts you
will need for your monster. You can take
one part from one kind of animal. Take
another part from another kind of animal.

What kind of head will your monster need?

Will it have a tail? What kind?

Will it need legs? How many?
Will it have wings and be a flying
monster? What kind of wings?
Will it have hair? What color will
it be? Think of the eyes, the ears,
and the nose.

Make a picture of the way your monster will look. You may paint the picture, or you may wish to draw one with crayons or colored chalk.

You can also make a cut-out monster from sheets of colored paper. A monster's body can be cut from one piece of paper. Its head can be cut from another piece. Paste bits of paper on the head for the monster's eyes, ears, nose, and mouth. Paste the legs and tail on the body.

As you paint, draw, cut, or paste, think how your monster would move about. Would it fly? Would it swim? Would it hop or crawl or run?

Think also about where it would live. Should it live in the deep, dark forest? Should it live in a cave in a mountain? Should it live on the bottom of a river? Should it live in a dark barn? Or in some place too terrible to think about?

To name your monster you can make up
a word—a word that has never been used.
You might make up the word by putting
together parts of two words.

If your monster is part cat and part
elephant, you might use one of these words.

EL-E-CAT

CAT-E-PHANT

A monster that is part dog and part
hippopotamus might be a **dogopotamus.**
What else might it be called?

When your monster has a name, you may
enjoy writing a story about it. Tell what
magic things your funny monster can do.
You and other children may want to make
a book, using the stories and pictures.

Can You Read This?

Part 1

Look at these monsters. What would you do if you saw one of them swimming in the water or walking on land? Would you be frightened?

These pictures show "make-believe" monsters. You may have read stories about monsters in books or in newspapers. You may have seen them on TV. Which ones have faces that look like the faces of people? Which ones have bodies that look like the bodies of animals? Which ones look like plants? What would you call the monster that looks as if it were made of boxes?

Part 2

Here are some real animals. Some lived long ago. Some live today. You may have read about them, or you may have seen them on TV. Which animals do not have feet or legs?

These pictures show odd-looking fish. Some people might call them monsters. Would you call them monsters? Why do you think some people might call them monsters?

These fish were found by men who wanted to learn more about things living in the sea. The men learned many things about these fish. They do not think of them as monsters.

113

1. What is Part 1 about?

   real animals   plants
   make-believe animals   fish

2. What is Part 2 about?

   real animals   plants
   make-believe animals   fish

3. Do you like to read about make-believe monsters? Why? *NO*

4. Do you like to read about real animals? Why? *Yes*

5. Do you always know what is real or what is make-believe? Why? *Yes*

R

Can you tell the real animal from the make-believe animal in these pictures?

M-B

When You Read

More Than One — Plural Forms

These words were in the selection about monsters. Each word means **more than one** thing. Read the words.

stories	feet	bodies
faces	books	boxes
fish	men	newspapers

If a word means **more than one** thing, we say it is a **plural form**.

Read the root words and the plural forms of these words.

face-faces   book-books

newspaper-newspapers   box-boxes

Which plural forms are made by adding **s** to the root word?

Which plural form is made by adding **es** to the root word?

Now read these words.

    story-stories   man-men   fish-fish
    body-bodies   foot-feet

Which plural forms are made by changing **y** to **i** and adding **es**?

Which plural form is the same as the word for **one** of these things?

What is the word for "more than one **foot**"? What is the plural form of **man**? What happened to the root words?

Try This

Read these sentences. Can you tell if the underlined word means **one** or **more than one** thing?

1. The sheep eat the grass.
2. The lady shopped for groceries.
3. The boy's teeth are very clean.
4. Buses took the children to school.
5. The monster had a face like a monkey's.

116

Museum Talk

Mrs. Winters was standing before her class. "Did you have fun at the museum yesterday?" she asked.

All the hands went up.

"Good!" said Mrs. Winters. "Jud, what did you like best?"

"The bones!" he said with a big smile. "They looked so real."

"What bones?" asked Penny. "I don't remember seeing any bones."

"Don't you remember the big whale?" asked Jud. "It was the biggest thing in the museum. And it was put together from real bones."

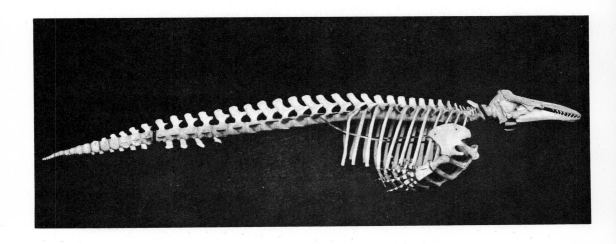

"I don't believe they were real bones," said Penny. "Were they, Mrs. Winters?"

"Yes, the whale bones were real ones," said Mrs. Winters. "They were found on the bottom of a sea."

"It must have been hard work putting all those bones together," said Kevin.

"I liked the rocks best," said Pete. "You see, I collect rocks, too. And I saw some of the same kinds of rocks that I have in my collection. But the museum has many kinds I had never seen before."

"That may be because the rocks in the museum came from all over the world," said Mrs. Winters.

"I know," answered Pete. "And all my rocks were found near home. But if I ever go to another part of the world, I'll look for kinds I can't find around here."

"I liked the rock collection, too,"
said Pete's friend. "I like the way they
put rocks of the same color together."

Mrs. Winters asked other children to
tell what they liked best. They talked
about stuffed animals, seashells, fish,
birds' nests, and many other things.

At last most of the children had talked
about things they had liked. But one boy
had kept still.

"Why so still, John?" asked the teacher.
"Didn't you see anything you liked?"

"I didn't see what I wanted to see,"
said John. "I was hoping to see a stamp
collection like the one I have. But I
didn't see even one stamp yesterday.
Don't museums keep stamp collections?"

"Some museums do," said Donna. "Let's
have a museum at school so John can bring
his stamps. May we plan one today?"

"Pete can bring his rock collection,
and I can bring all my shells," said Pam.

"I can bring my postcards," said Linda.
"I have cards from many of our big cities."

"I can bring my doll collection,"
said Janet. "I collect dolls from other
countries, but I have just five so far."

"Well," said Mrs. Winters. "From the
sound of things, I think it's all planned.
Bring your collections, and we will set
them up. Then we will ask your families
to come to a grand opening of the museum."

"May our grandmothers and grandfathers
come too?" Kathy wanted to know.

"And our little brothers and sisters?"
asked Jud.

"Yes," said Mrs. Winters. "Ask anyone
in your family—all but little babies."

The children clapped. They liked the
idea of a school museum. They liked
having their families come to school, too.

About Stamps

John was proud of his stamp collection. Not only had he collected many stamps, but he also knew a lot about stamps.

When John took his stamp collection to school, his teacher let him tell about the first stamps that were ever printed.

On the next five pages, you can read some of the things John had learned about stamps.

Today letters must have stamps if they
are sent in the mail. Stamps are our way
of paying someone to carry our letters
to the people we are writing to.

But people have not always had stamps.
Long ago, people who sent letters to their
friends and families did not use stamps.
In those days, people who got the letters
had to pay for having them delivered.

This plan worked all right when people
who got the letters were willing to pay.
But those who carried the mail never knew
if they would be paid or not.

Sometimes the one who was to get a
letter didn't have money to pay for it.
Or he may have died or moved far away.
Then there was nobody to pay for having
the letter delivered. Many letters were
carried for miles and miles with nobody
to pay for them at the other end. Can you
see how this would worry those who carried
the mail?

Some people wanted to have letters paid for by the ones who sent them, not by those who got them. But this plan worried people, too. If they paid first, they were afraid someone would keep the money and never deliver the letters.

Then, more than a hundred years ago, a man in England had a plan for a better way to pay for sending letters.

This man gave the world the idea of using stamps to mail letters. He wanted the one who sent a letter to pay for it. He could pay by buying a stamp for each letter he wanted to mail. He would then put the stamp on the outside of the letter.

At first people did not like the idea of letter stamps. But as they studied the plan, they began to understand it, and they were willing to try it. The first mail stamps were printed, and people in England began to use them.

The stamps were printed on sheets of paper, many small stamps on one sheet. People paid a penny for each stamp. Each stamp had to be cut from the sheet and put on the outside of the letter.

Before long, the new stamps were named the Penny Blacks. Why do you think they were called that?

At first, Penny Blacks were made only in England. But before long, the idea of mail stamps spread to the United States.

In the picture you can see the first
two mail stamps made in the United States.
One is a five-penny stamp, and the other
is a ten-penny stamp.

Sometimes the people who sold stamps
ran out of five-penny stamps. Then they
cut a ten-penny stamp into two pieces
and used them for two five-penny stamps.

Today's stamps are not too different
from the very first ones printed in the
United States. Many of our stamps still
have pictures of famous men. And we still
stick a stamp on a letter to show that the
one who sent it has paid for its delivery.

Collecting Stamps

From the time the first Penny Blacks
were printed, many people have enjoyed
collecting stamps. Boys and girls and
older people, too, save them, trade them,
and stick them in stamp books.

Why do so many people collect stamps?
Some enjoy having sets of tiny colored
pictures. Some like to collect things
from far-away countries. And some of us
just like to save anything we can get free.

You can begin a stamp collection by asking your friends and family to save old, used envelopes for you. When you get some, look them over and keep the ones with stamps stuck on the outside.

Next, cut off the stamp corner of each envelope. Do not try to pull the stamps off the envelope paper. To get them off, leave the stamp corners in water all night. By morning, the stamps will come right off the paper.

Then lay the wet stamps on soft paper. Put more soft paper over them. A book on top will keep them flat as they dry.

Most mail stamps have words or letters
that tell the country where the stamps
were made and sold. All of your stamps
may be marked "U.S." or "United States."
Or some may be marked with names of other
countries, near and far.

Stamps are also marked to show how
much they cost. Some cost only a penny,
but most of them cost more.

In a short time,
you may have many
different kinds of
stamps. Pick up
one and study the
picture. Try to
read the words on
the stamp.

This boy is using
a glass to help him
see what is on the
tiny stamp.

When you have ten or more stamps, you will want to sort them. They can be sorted by color, or by how much they cost. They can also be sorted by the kinds of pictures on them. Look for stamps with pictures of things such as these:

famous people   flowers   animals

stars or planets   famous places   birds

When your stamps are sorted, you can begin a stamp book. Stamp books at a dime store do not cost very much. But if you can't buy one, you can make one from sheets of plain white paper.

If you like to collect stamps, you may enjoy collecting them as long as you live. Many people do.

Shells and Other Things

Donna lives in a small city, far from the sea. Yet Donna collects seashells.

It all started one summer when Donna and her family made a trip. They went to the shore for two short, but happy, days.

The shells Donna picked up were dead things. But at one time, they were parts of living, growing animals.

In the picture, you see a snail that lives in the sea. The soft parts of the snail's body are inside its shell. The shell guards the snail from many dangers. The snail can just pull in its head and hide.

The shell of a sea snail is all in
one piece. Donna found many kinds of
these one-part shells. The snail family
is a big one, and so Donna looked for
many different kinds of snail shells.

Another kind of sea animal has a shell
that is in two parts. In the pictures you
see a living clam with its shell open and
with it shut. The shell guards the clam
from many dangers.

When sea animals, like snails and clams,
die, their shells come off. The water
of the sea carries the shells up to the
shore. The sun dries them, and the wind
and sand make them smooth and shiny.

Donna keeps her shells in egg cartons.
Her one-part shells are in one carton and
her two-part shells are in another carton.
For a good collection, she would never
think of mixing the two kinds of shells.

After Donna has sorted her shells,
she tries to find out what kind of sea
animal lived in each one. She could find
this out at a big museum. But there is
no museum in Donna's city, and so she
uses the city library.

The librarian shows Donna where the children's books about shells are kept. Donna finds books she likes very much. So she shows her library card, and the librarian lets her take three books home.

With the books under her arm, Donna walks home. Back home, she looks in her books. She finds pictures and names of many shells. When she finds the name of one of her shells, she prints it on a card. In time, she hopes to have a name card for each shell in her collection.

Some people pick up shells, stuff them
in a pocket or desk, and forget about them.
Those who do that end up with a lot of
junk. But that is not Donna's way at all.
She wants a real collection, not junk.

Donna has sorted her shells, learned
about them, and found a way to show them
off. She is proud of her collection.
She has fun with it, and she did not
have to buy a thing.

In the picture you see other things
that are free. If you want to start a
collection you may get an idea from it.

Toy Banks, Dolls, and Model Kits

People collect many different kinds
of things. Fine collections can be made
from things that are free. But some
people collect things they have to buy.

Have you ever heard of collecting banks?
This is what a father and his son collect.
The banks are painted in bright colors
and are made in odd shapes. Some have
moving parts. When a penny or dime is
dropped into these banks, the parts move.

The father has fun buying the banks,
and the son has fun playing with them.

138

A girl and her mother collect old dolls.
Some of the dolls they bought are made of
wood. Others they bought have arms, legs,
and bodies that are stuffed. The old legs
and arms can still be moved.

One of the oldest dolls has a face
made of wax. The wax face looks very
real. Dolls with wax faces are so old
that many people have never seen or
heard of them.

Another old doll has a china head,
as bright and shiny as a new china dish.
Many old dolls have blue china eyes that
open and shut. And some have real hair.

Many boys, and some girls too, collect models. Model cars, planes, and rockets are the ones they like best. The models are small, but they still look real.

Some children buy model kits at a toy store or dime store. Then they have the fun of building their models. Some kits have so many pieces that children are not able to put them together without help.

If kits are hard for you to work with, you may be wise to start your collection with small models that are all made. Then as you grow older, you will be able to build your own models.

You may say, "How can I ever collect anything I have to buy? I have no money."

Have you ever tried to earn money for something you want? Some children your age think it is not too early in life to earn money by doing small jobs.

One strong boy helps his older brother deliver groceries. He saves some of the money in the bank. Another boy sometimes gets up early to help sort and deliver morning papers. He uses his money for model kits. Many girls, only a little older than you, are able to earn money by helping to care for smaller children. Some use their money to buy doll dresses.

If you want to collect something that must be bought, you may have to earn all or part of the money. But what if you are a bit too small to find a job? Then you would be wiser to collect things that are free. Remember, that can be fun, too.

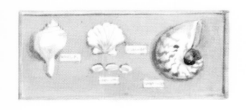

Picture 1

Can You Read This?

When people have collected things, they like to look at their things. They like to show them, and they want other people to look at their collections, too. Sheets of paper or boxes can be used to show collections. If a collection is placed where it can be seen, it can be enjoyed by many people. (See Picture 1.)

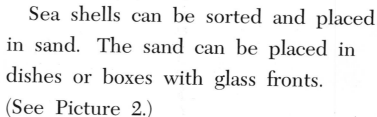

Sea shells can be sorted and placed in sand. The sand can be placed in dishes or boxes with glass fronts. (See Picture 2.)

Picture 2

Picture 3

Picture collections can be pasted on paper, on cans, or on boxes. They can be used to make a room look brighter. (See Picture 3.)

142

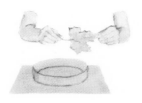

Picture 4

1. Place leaf on paper. Put a cardboard ring around leaf.
2. Fill the ring with plaster.
3. When the plaster dries and gets hard, turn the mold upside down. Take the leaf and ring from the mold. Paint mold.

Things that are hard to keep can be molded in plaster. A collection of the plaster molds can be made. (See Picture 4.)

It takes work and time to make a collection. But it is fun to show collections to other people.

1. Tell how you can show a collection of seashells, or pictures, or leaves.
2. How did the pictures help you learn how to show collections?

When You Read

(To be read with the teacher)

Root Words and Suffixes

Read these sentences. See how the underlined words are spelled.

1. You can <u>paste</u> pictures on colored paper.
2. The boys were <u>pasting</u> pictures in school.
3. You can <u>dry</u> flowers in warm sand.
4. <u>Dried</u> flowers are pretty.
5. It was John's turn to <u>bat</u>.
6. He <u>batted</u> the ball and ran to first base.

Read the underlined words in the first two sentences. The root word is <u>paste</u>. What suffix is added to make the other word? How was the suffix added?

Read the underlined words in sentences 3 and 4. What is the root word? How is the suffix added?

144

Read the underlined word in sentences
5 and 6. <u>Bat</u> is a root word. How is
the suffix added?

Suffixes are added to root words to make
other words. Knowing the root word
can help you figure out the word with
a suffix.

Try This

Read these sentences. Look at each
underlined word. Tell what the root word
is. Tell how the suffix is added to the
root word.

1. The baby was <u>crying</u>.
2. The baby <u>cries</u> for food.
3. Jane <u>cried</u> when she fell from the swing.
4. Paper <u>dropped</u> to the floor.
5. Linda was <u>dropping</u> the paper.

Suffixes Add Meaning

The word **boy** means **one boy**. **Boys** means **more than one boy**. What suffix is added to **boy** to change its meaning?

You know what the word **big** means. What does the word **bigger** mean? How does the **er** change the meaning of **big**?

What do the suffixes in the underlined words add to the meaning of **bird**?

The egg was in the bird's nest.

The birds were in the tree.

The birds' eggs were in the nests.

Try This

Read these sentences.

1. The girls played in Jill's yard.
2. The girls' dolls were smaller than Jill's.
3. Tom is shorter than Bill.

Tell what suffix is added to each underlined word. Tell what the suffix adds to the word meaning.

The Brothers Grimm

Many people like to collect things. Some collect stamps, some pick up colored seashells, some save rocks.

A long time ago two brothers named Grimm decided to do a different kind of collecting. They collected old stories.

The stories the two brothers collected were old ones that people had told for hundreds of years. No one knew who made up these stories, or when they were first told. Many of the people who told the stories could not read or write.

Fathers and mothers told the stories
to children. When the children grew up,
they remembered most of the stories.
Then these children told the same stories
when they became fathers and mothers and
grandfathers and grandmothers.

This went on for many hundreds of years,
yet no one ever wrote the stories down.
They were remembered, not from reading
them, but from hearing them told.

As time went by, more people learned
to read and write. They had books with
new stories. Soon only a few old people
remembered the old stories. And those
who remembered them were growing old.

The Grimms were afraid that when the old people died, the old tales would die with them. That was why the brothers decided to collect the tales. But first they had to find the few people who still remembered them.

And so the two Grimms set out, with packs on their backs, walking from farm to farm. They asked around, hoping to find old people who could remember and tell the old, old stories.

Every time a tale was told, one of the brothers wrote it down. He tried to use the very words the storyteller used.

Not all of the old people were willing
to tell their stories to two big men.
One old woman knew many tales, but she
could tell them only to children. So the
Grimms decided to bring a few children
to the old woman's home.

As soon as the children were sitting around
her, she began, "Once upon a time ——."
Then she went on to tell story after story.
One brother sneaked in and hid so he could
write down the tales as she told them.

After five years of walking from town
to town and from farm to farm, the Grimms
had collected 86 tales. Their first book
of old stories was ready to be printed.
From the time the first book came out,
children everywhere enjoyed the tales.

The brothers kept collecting tales until
they had three books, filled with 210 tales.
Today, more than 150 years later, children
still enjoy these tales, which are printed
in just about every country in the world.

The Giant Beet

A very poor farmer once planted beet
seeds in his field. Only one of the seeds
grew, but that beet grew so fast that the
farmer could see it grow. Its stem was
as tall as a tree. When its leaves began
to unroll, they looked like big umbrellas.

As the days went by, the beet grew
bigger and bigger and redder and redder.
The farmer could not believe his eyes,
the beet was so big. It was indeed the
finest beet the farmer had ever seen.

153

"What can I do with that giant beet?"
thought the farmer. "It's much too grand
to be used as food. And I could never
bring myself to sell anything so grand.
What terrible luck for a poor man like me!"

Day and night the farmer worried about
his giant beet. But, as he thought more
about it, he decided what he should do.

"Why, I'll take it to the king! He
should be pleased to have it. I'll put
it in my cart and take it to the castle."

He loaded the beet into his two-wheel
cart and crawled on top. Then the old
cart, pulled by his two tired old oxen,
bumped and jiggled down the road.

When the king first saw the giant beet,
he began to stare. Could it be real?

"This beet is much too grand for me,"
said the farmer. "I will give it to you,
for it is the finest beet in the world."

"Indeed it is," agreed the king.
"I am proud and happy to have it."

The king now stared at the farmer.
How poor he looked! Yet here he was,
giving away what he himself needed.

The king wanted to thank the farmer
for being so kind and good. He saw the
farmer needed more than kind words. So
he gave him a new house, new fields, and
two strong oxen to help with the plowing.

155

Now it happened that the poor farmer
had a rich brother. He was not only rich,
but also very greedy. As soon as he
heard about his brother's good luck,
he became very angry.

"Why should my brother have all the
good luck?" he thought. "Just because
he gave the king a big old beet? I can
think of better things than beets to give
the king. I'll give him my finest horse."

Tickled by his own idea, he lost no
time. He got into his fine wagon, which
was pulled by a team of milk-white oxen.
Then, with the best horse following, he
was at the castle in no time at all.

The king took the horse, which was indeed as fine a one as he had ever seen. Then he looked the farmer up and down.

"I can see you are not a man who needs money or land," said the king. "But I do want to give you something. I have it! I'll give you something very rare."

The greedy brother was so happy he could not speak. He stood with his mouth open, waiting to see what he would get.

The king went on, "Yes, I have decided to give you a giant beet! There it is! You must agree that no other beet is so rare. And thank you for the fine horse. I can use it to pull my carriage."

The king walked away with the horse.
And the rich, greedy farmer, who was now
very angry indeed, did the only thing he
could do. He loaded the big beet into
his wagon and headed for home.

"Ach, me," he thought. "I could kick
myself. My brother has all the luck.
This beet that made him rich is the ruin
of me. It cost me my very best horse."

A Trip to Lubber Land

I will never forget my trip
to Lubber Land. It was long,
long ago, when houses could fly
like birds, and when rabbits
could talk as well as you and I.
It was the time when foxes and
squirrels played together and
snow was black. It was when
tadpoles lived in beehives
and wasps lived in ponds.

I'm sure you won't believe
the things I saw in Lubber Land!
How could you, if you have never
been there?

As I walked down a road, I met a goat. It was coming from the flour mill with a hundred sacks of flour on its back.

As I walked on, I came to a tree. I'm sure you have never seen such a pretty sight, for it was a pancake tree. Oh, how the bees were buzzing around it!

Pancakes were growing like leaves from the tree. And the pancakes were hot with melted butter on them. Under the tree was a jar of jam, all ready for a pancake party.

Oh, what a feast that was! Lunch and dinner every day were real treats.

I came next to a place where animals
were baking cakes. Two brown donkeys
had ground the wheat into flour. Three
little pigs had mixed flour with milk and
eggs to make the cakes. And a black cow
was sliding them into the hot oven.

Oh, yes, I must remember to tell you
that the donkeys and pigs had on red shoes
—not black shoes, but pretty red ones.
And the cow had a hat with yellow flowers.

I saw even more, but you would never
believe me if I told you, would you?
But I'll tell you anyway.

I saw a forest cutting down its own trees, one by one. Have you ever heard of such a thing?

And I saw a big farm with no farmers. The farm was plowing its own fields and planting its own seeds. And the plows needed no oxen to pull them.

And there is one last thing I just have to tell. In all of Lubber Land, not one rooster could crow. But early every morning, just as the sun came up, all the hens cried out:

Cock-a-doodle-doo, my friend,
Now this silly tale must end.

The Sweet Porridge

There was once a girl who was good and kind, but very poor. Many nights she and her mother had to go to bed hungry. Finally, there was no food anywhere in the house, and they were miserable indeed.

In the hope of finding some ripe berries or nuts, the girl took a basket and went out to the forest.

As the girl came to the forest, a kind
voice took her by surprise. She turned
around to see an old woman in a long skirt.
Somehow or other, the woman knew how very
miserable the girl and her mother were.

"I want to give you this," the woman
said, handing the girl a round black pot.
Then she began to explain how to use it.

"Take it home and put it on the stove,"
she explained. "Then speak these words:
'Cook, little pot, cook.' At once it will
cook up a supper of good sweet porridge.
When you and your mother have had enough
porridge, say: 'Stop, little pot, stop.'
And the pot will stop cooking until the
next time you speak to it."

The girl thanked the woman kindly, put the pot under her arm, and carried it home. Then, as quickly as she could, she put the pot on the kitchen stove.

"Cook, little pot, cook," she said in a stern voice. The pot quickly began to cook good sweet porridge.

The girl and her mother each got a spoon and ate dish after dish of porridge. When they had had enough, the girl said, "Stop, little pot, stop." She had hardly said the last word when the cooking stopped.

The days of hard times were over for the girl and her mother. Each day they ate as much sweet porridge as they could, and they were able to work long and hard.

One day the mother felt hungry when the girl happened to be away from home. "I don't really have to wait for her to come back," the mother thought. "Surely I am wise enough to make the pot cook."

She put the pot on the stove and said in a stern voice, "Cook, little pot, cook." She had hardly said the last word before the sweet smell of porridge filled the air.

Soon the woman had enough porridge. But for the life of her, she could not make the cooking stop. She really tried, but she always said the wrong words.

Porridge soon ran out of the pot, over onto the stove, and down to the floor. And the pot went right on cooking more.

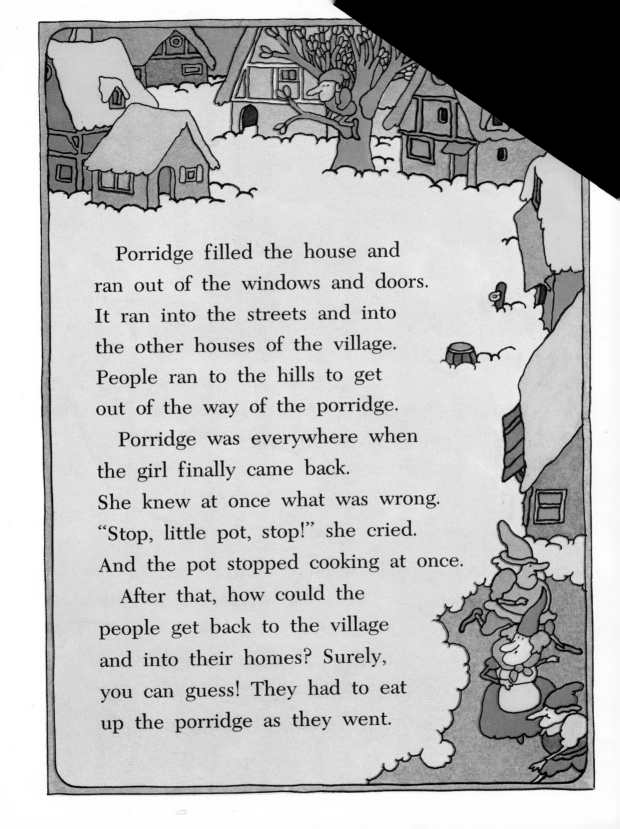

Porridge filled the house and
ran out of the windows and doors.
It ran into the streets and into
the other houses of the village.
People ran to the hills to get
out of the way of the porridge.

Porridge was everywhere when
the girl finally came back.
She knew at once what was wrong.
"Stop, little pot, stop!" she cried.
And the pot stopped cooking at once.

After that, how could the
people get back to the village
and into their homes? Surely,
you can guess! They had to eat
up the porridge as they went.

Clever Elsa

Once upon a time there was a girl called Clever Elsa. When she grew up, a man named Hans fell in love with her and made her his wife.

Elsa's nose was too long, her hands were too red, her ears stuck out, and her hair was the color of mud.

"You may not be as pretty as other girls," said Hans to Elsa. "But you are clever, and I think that is much better than being pretty. Who else but you can hear butterflies walk on flowers?"

Elsa and Hans were living on a farm. The wheat was ready to be cut, but Hans had no time to do it.

Early one morning he said to Elsa, "I must go off to town again today to earn some money. Will you be able to go into the field and cut the wheat?"

"Of course, I will, Hans. I'll be glad to do it," said Elsa quickly.

Hans rode off, and Elsa packed a big lunch for herself and took it with her to the wheat field.

Once in the field, she began to think. She sat down and thought hard, for she wanted to be sure to do the right thing.

"I can either eat now, or work now," she thought. "I wonder, should I eat now and then work afterwards? Or should I work first and eat afterwards?"

She finally decided to eat first. But after she ate, she felt very tired.

"Should I work now, and sleep later?" she asked. "Or should I sleep now and work afterwards? Work ahead of sleep, or sleep ahead of work? I think I should sleep now."

In a little while she was fast asleep.

When Elsa woke up, the stars were out. She knew she was not in her soft feather bed, but she did not know where she was.

Elsa jumped to her feet and cried out, "This is not where I live! I wonder, am I really Elsa, or am I someone else? I am clever, so surely I can tell who I am."

But no matter how hard she thought, she still could not answer her question. But she finally had an idea. "I'll go to the farmhouse and see if I'm home."

Elsa ran. But when she came to the house, she found all the doors and windows shut for the night. She felt miserable.

"Now what?" she said. "Am I behind that door, or am I here? I must find out."

So she rapped on the door and called,
"Is Clever Elsa at home?"

Hans, who had come home very late,
thought Elsa was sleeping in her bed.
So Hans yelled from behind the door,
"Of course, she is! She is sound asleep
in her soft feather bed," Hans explained.

"Ach, I was afraid of that," said Elsa.
With tears in her eyes, she turned sadly
away. "If Elsa is really in her bed, then
I can't be Elsa. I must be another girl,
and I must belong to another house."

She ran away, fast and far, and only
the stars above ever knew where she went.
Every once in a while, people would ask,
"What do you think has happened to Elsa?"

They never saw her again, but they
never really worried about her either.
For they knew, as you surely know, how
clever she was. And any girl as clever
as Elsa can always take care of herself.

The Elves and the Shoemaker

This is a play that is told in two parts.
The people who are needed for the play are:

Storyteller
Shoemaker
Shoemaker's Wife
A Man
A Lady
Two Elves

Part 1 — The Shoemaker's Surprise

STORYTELLER: Do you believe in elves? You will when we tell you what happened long ago and far away in a shoemaker's shop. Until now, it's been a secret.

SHOEMAKER: Ach, when I think of all the fine shoes I have made! People used to come from all over just to buy my shoes. But now times are very hard indeed.

WIFE: But you still work hard. Your luck will change one of these days.

SHOEMAKER: But the harder I work, the poorer we get. Now I have just enough leather for one pair of shoes.

WIFE: Don't worry, dear. We are not ruined yet. Come, let us go to sleep.

SHOEMAKER: I'll just cut my leather and lay the pieces on the bench with my tools. I'll finish the shoes in the morning.

STORYTELLER: The shoemaker cut up a piece
of leather for his last pair of shoes.
When he had finished, he followed his
wife up to bed. The next morning, the
wife got up bright and early.

WIFE: My poor man! Today he must make
his last pair of shoes. I only hope
that someone will come and buy them.
Now, let me see, what can I find to
cook for breakfast?

SHOEMAKER (coming into the room):
Good morning, wife. Is breakfast ready?
I must eat quickly and get to work on
that last pair of shoes.

WIFE (looking at the bench where there is a pair of shoes in place of the leather): Why, the shoes are finished! And they are the best ones you have ever made.

SHOEMAKER: You must be wrong, dear wife. All I did last night was cut the leather.

WIFE: But, but you must have made them! I'm sure I did not! Look at them.

SHOEMAKER (looking at the shoes): Can I make shoes in my sleep? I don't know who made them, but he did a fine job.

WIFE: I'll put them in the shop window. Maybe someone will see them and buy.

STORYTELLER: Filled with hope, the shoemaker and his wife sat down to watch the door of the shop. They held their breaths when a well-dressed man came in.

MAN: I must buy some shoes for my wife. May I see the ones in the window?

SHOEMAKER (handing him the shoes): Here you are, sir. Do look them over well. Feel them, too. You can tell they were made from a fine piece of leather.

MAN: Never in my life have I seen such fine shoes. I'll pay you two times what you are asking. (The man pays for the shoes and leaves the shop.)

WIFE: That's far more than you have ever been paid for one pair of shoes.

SHOEMAKER: Now I can buy enough leather for two more pairs. I'll cut them out tonight and begin work on them tomorrow.

STORYTELLER: And that is what he did.
He bought the leather and cut it out.
But when the shoemaker and his wife
came down the next morning, they found
the two pairs of shoes all made.

SHOEMAKER (coming into the room with his
wife): So! Again last night, someone
came in, used my tools, and made
shoes for me. Who do you guess it was?

WIFE: No matter who, he makes fine shoes.
I'll put them in the window, and let us
hope that the new pairs will sell.

STORYTELLER: After the shoes had been put
in the shop window, the man and woman
sat down to wait. In a little while
a pretty lady opened the door.

LADY: Good day. May I please look at the
pretty shoes you have in your window?
They may be just what my girls need.

WIFE (handing her the shoes): Take your
time and look the shoes over well.
Feel the leather, see the fine work.

LADY: I have never seen such fine shoes!
I'll take the two pairs. I'm sure my
two girls will love them. I'll pay
you two times what you are asking.
(The lady pays for the shoes, picks
them up, and turns to open the door.)
I'll tell all my friends to come here
to buy themselves some shoes.

SHOEMAKER: Thank you very much. (He
waves as the lady leaves.)

SHOEMAKER: Wife, now I can buy enough
leather for four pairs of shoes.

WIFE (dancing around the floor): What
good luck we are having! We will soon
be able to have new shoes ourselves.
Come, let us dance.

SHOEMAKER: Yes, let's dance. (He takes
his wife's hand and together they dance.)

STORYTELLER: For a long while, that is the
way things went. Every night, the old
shoemaker would cut out the leather
and leave the pieces on his bench.
Every morning he would find a row of
pretty, well-made shoes. As more and
more people came to buy, the shoemaker
got more and more money. He and his
wife soon became rich.

End of Part 1

Part 2—The Tiny Shoemaker

STORYTELLER: As time went on, the shoemaker
and his wife wondered more and more
about who was making the pairs of shoes.
One cold night, in the dead of winter,
the shoemaker had an idea.

SHOEMAKER: Wife, I'm going to stay down
in the shop all night. I must find
out who is making all those shoes.

WIFE: Then I'll stay down with you. If
we hide behind the chair in the corner,
we can keep our eyes on the workbench.

SHOEMAKER (speaking in a stern voice):
We must be as still as two scared mice.
We will speak only in whispers.

STORYTELLER: Like mice, they sneaked behind
the chair and waited. The only sounds
in the shop were their soft whispers.
Then, just at midnight, two tiny men
hopped in. They jumped up on the bench
and started to work. The shoemaker and
his wife held their breaths.

ELVES: We tap, tap, tap
On pieces of leather
We rap, rap, rap
And put a shoe together.

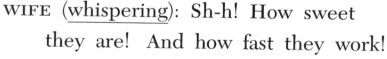

SHOEMAKER (whispering): Look at them.
They're two tiny elves!

WIFE (whispering): Sh-h! How sweet
they are! And how fast they work!

ELVES: We work and smile
    And laugh at ourselves
    We dance a while,
    Two happy little elves!

STORYTELLER: The elves danced around, and
    the shoemaker and his wife watched.
    Then, as quickly as they had come in,
    the elves jumped out the windows.

WIFE: Oh, the poor little men. They
    went out into the cold winter night!

SHOEMAKER: And think how hard they have
    worked for us. How can we thank them?

WIFE: Did you see how poorly they were
    dressed? Their outfits could never
    keep out the cold. I'll make them
    snug little outfits—pants, jackets,
    fur caps, everything!

SHOEMAKER: And I'll make each a pair of
    shoes from the best leather I can buy.

STORYTELLER: The shoemaker and his wife
worked for days on the new outfits.
Finally they were finished.

SHOEMAKER: Look, wife! Tonight I put
out the tiny shoes in place of leather.

WIFE (getting other parts of the outfits):
And I will lay out the rest of the
things—pants, jackets, and caps.

SHOEMAKER: Would you like to hide in the
corner and watch for them?

WIFE: Of course I would!

STORYTELLER: So once again the man and his
wife hid and watched. And again, just
at midnight, the two tiny elves came.
They went quickly to the workbench,
looking for leather. How overjoyed
they were to find, not leather, but
snug little outfits. They quickly
put them on, then danced and sang.

ELVES: Now we are well-dressed little men. Never will we work again!

STORYTELLER: They sang the same little song over and over, and finally they danced right out the window.

WIFE: I wonder, will the elves ever come back again?

SHOEMAKER: No, wife, I think not.

STORYTELLER: He was right, for the elves never came back. But from that time on, the shoemaker and his wife had only good luck. And they kept the story about the elves their secret until now, when they told it to you.

More Tales in the Grimm Collection

The next time you go to a library, you may enjoy looking for other stories in the Grimm collection. The names of three of their stories are on this and the next page. Read about these three stories and decide which one you would most enjoy reading. Then try to find the story in your library.

The Frog Prince

This story is about a frog, who was once a prince. Before he can be turned into a prince again, he must find a princess who will love him. Will he find that princess?

Rapunzel

A girl with long, long yellow hair is made to stay high in the top of a castle, far from everyone she loves. In this story you will find out how her long hair and a prince save her.

Snow White and Rose Red

What would you do if a bear came to your house? Would you let it in? Snow White and Rose Red did, and they were kind to it, too. Can you guess what happened?

Can You Read This?

Part 1

There are many kinds of stories that people have told for hundreds of years. Some of these stories have magic in them. Silly or frightened people become wise, brave, or strong by magic. Hungry people get food by magic. Poor people get rich by magic. Can you remember any stories like these?

Some stories tell about people who do things that you would not think they could do. People who are silly do wise or clever things. People who are wise or clever do silly or wrong things. Frightened little people face danger bravely. Do you know any stories like these?

There are stories that try to teach a <u>lesson</u>. Do you remember the story about the lion and the mouse? The mouse said he would remember the lion if the lion set him free. When the lion fell into a net, the mouse remembered him. The mouse began to gnaw the knots in the net, until he had chewed them enough to set the lion free. What lesson does this story try to teach? Can you remember any other stories that teach a lesson?

Many stories tell why or how something happened. Some of these stories are "make-believe" stories. One of these stories tells why the bear has a short tail. Another tells why the lion roars. Have you read any stories like these?

Part 2

In the library you can find many of the stories that people have told for hundreds of years. In the part of the library where children's books are kept, you will see many books that you can read.

Next, you will want to know where to
find the kind of books you want to read.
All books of one kind are kept in one place.
In one part of the children's library,
there are stories that people have told for
hundreds of years. These stories are also
put together as magic stories, why and how
stories, stories about people who do things
you wouldn't think they could do, and
stories that try to teach something.

When you know the kind of books you
want to read, the librarian will be glad
to help you find them. The library has
books about everything.

1. What would be a good title for Part 1?
2. What kinds of stories does this selection
   tell about?
3. What would be a good title for Part 2?

When You Read

(To be read with the teacher)

Two Consonants for One Sound

These words were in the selection you just read. Can you read them now?

silly	wrong	know
knot	lesson	gnaw

In each word there are two consonant letters that stand for one sound. In which words do the same two letters stand for one consonant sound? What sound does **ll** in **silly** stand for? What sound does **ss** in **lesson** stand for?

Read the word that has the same first sound as **run**. What two letters in **wrong** stand for the first sound?

Read the three words that have the same first sound as **net**. What two letters stand for the first sound in **know**? What two letters stand for the first sound in **knot**?

What two letters stand for the first sound in **gnaw**?

The words **gnaw** and **lesson** are new words. Do you know what they mean? How did you figure out their meaning?

Sometimes two consonant letters together stand for one consonant sound.

Try This

Read these sentences. Then read each underlined word. Tell which two letters in each word stand for one consonant sound. You can tell the meaning of each underlined word from its use in the sentence.

1. Dogs like to gnaw on old shoes.
2. Ted has a new wrist watch.
3. Jeff had a cut on his knee.
4. Did you hear a knock at the door?
5. A wren builds its nest near houses.

Going Places

Afternoon Traffic

It was a hot, summer afternoon, and Mark and his father were on their way back from the country. They were hot and tired, and they had hoped to get home before dark. But with the traffic as bad as it was, they began to think the sun would set long before they got there.

"A turtle can go faster than this," said Mark. "Do you think there has been an accident up ahead?"

"I don't know," said Mark's father. "But I hear a helicopter flying above us. Maybe we can get a traffic report."

Father snapped on the car radio. "And now to Helicopter 3 for the traffic report," came the voice on the radio.

"This is Helicopter 3 now, flying over the Garden Freeway," came the next voice on the radio. "A bad four-car accident near Flower Street Exit has blocked the traffic going east. Traffic going east is backed up for about ten miles."

Father turned off the radio. "From the sound of that," he said, "we will have bumper-to-bumper traffic for the next ten miles if we stay on the freeway. I vote to turn off at the next exit and take the narrow back road home. Do you agree?"

"I vote the same way," said Mark.

Mark looked up at the helicopter.
"Boy, it must be fun to fly one of those,"
he said. "No bumper-to-bumper traffic.
Do you think I could fly a helicopter
and be a traffic reporter when I grow up?"

"If you study hard and make good grades
in school," Father answered. "But this
morning you wanted to be a farmer."

"That was just when I was on the farm.
Now I think it would be more fun to fly
helicopters and be a traffic reporter."

"But remember yesterday," said Father.
"Yesterday you wanted to be a singer."

"I still want to be a singer," said
Mark. "I could sing the traffic reports."

"You're a funny boy," said Mark's dad.
"It really wouldn't surprise me if you
became a zoo keeper somewhere. Monkeys
like you belong in a zoo."

Mark smiled. He <u>liked</u> it when his
father teased him.

Mark was still watching the helicopter.
Now it was just a tiny spot in the sky.

In a little while, they came to the
Spring Street exit where they turned off
the freeway. They were glad to see the
back road free of traffic.

"Well, at last we are out of the jam,"
said Father. "Now we can make better time."

Mark looked back at the sun sinking in
the west. The sky was a blaze of color.
"We will be almost home before dark," Mark
said. "For once, this narrow back road
is faster than the freeway. But had it
not been for the helicopter, we wouldn't
have known that we could try it."

Whirlybirds at Work

When a helicopter is ready to take off, its rotor blades begin to turn. They turn, they spin, they whirl around. With its rotor blades whirling fast, the helicopter takes off, straight up into the air.

Once a helicopter is in the air, it can fly near the ground or high above it. It can fly straight ahead, straight back, or sideways. It can even stay in one spot in the air and turn all the way around!

Some of the men who fly helicopters call them whirlybirds. Why do you think they are called that?

Many cities find helicopters useful in keeping traffic moving. By flying over a city, a helicopter policeman sees where traffic is blocked.

If he spots an accident, he reports
it at once so help can be sent to anyone
who is hurt. Other policemen are then
sent out to help keep traffic moving
around the accident.

The helicopter policeman reports
anything that may be a danger to drivers.
He tells which streets have not yet been
cleared of snow. He tells which roads
are under fog. He also reports places
where men are working on the road.

Traffic reports are very helpful to
drivers. The reports help drivers to be
more careful as they drive.

In some of our big cities, helicopters carry people to and from airports outside the city. The trip from the airport to the middle of the city is faster by helicopter than by car or bus.

Helicopters can land in mid-town because they do not need long runways. They take off by flying straight up into the air. They can land by coming straight down on almost anything flat and smooth. In some big cities, helicopters take off and land on the tops of tall buildings.

Helicopters are also useful on farms. Because they can fly close to the ground, they are used in spraying trees and other plants. Sometimes helicopters are used on farms to spread seeds over the soil.

In the west, many cowboys no longer ride horses. Today the cowboys sometimes ride in whirlybirds. At round-up time, animals are rounded up by helicopters.

Helicopters are also useful in finding lost animals. And in times of deep snow, when farm animals have trouble finding enough to eat, food is dropped to them from helicopters.

The picture shows a man who is in trouble. The water is getting higher, and his life is in danger.

But the man can be thankful that help has come. The helicopter will pull him up carefully, and the man will be safe.

A helicopter cannot fly as fast, or as far, as a big plane. It cannot seat as many people as a train or a city bus. Yet in some ways helicopters are more useful than planes, trains, or city buses. Many times, using a helicopter is the best way to do a job. Sometimes it is the only way.

Trains

Did you ever see a toy train that runs
along on a track? Did you notice that
the cars were not all alike? Did you
notice how many cars the train had?

A train can be made up of many cars.
Passenger cars are used to carry people,
or passengers. Freight cars are used to
carry goods, or freight. Some passenger
trains can even have a few freight cars.
Mail is one kind of freight that is
carried in passenger trains.

Passenger trains have cars for sitting and cars for sleeping. There are also cars where passengers can have breakfast, lunch, and dinner as the trains speed along.

People can travel by train from one coast of our big country to the other. But few people do that today. A trip from the East Coast to the West Coast takes about four days on a train. But it takes only about four hours by plane, So most people travel the faster way.

Today, most passenger trains are used for shorter trips. People who live a short way from the city ride a train into the city to work or shop. Then they do not have to worry about busy traffic or finding places to park their cars.

Subway trains are also used for short
trips. A subway is a railroad that runs
under the ground. In big New York City,
thousands of people ride the subway right
under the busy streets and tall buildings.

People who travel by subway walk down
the stairs to get underground. They wait
for the subway train. They hear it and
see its bright light as it comes rolling
down the track. When the train stops,
the doors open and the people get on.

At busy times, many subway passengers
must stand. That is why some subway cars
have so few seats. With fewer seats,
there is more standing room, and more
people can get into the train.

Not all subway rides are smooth rides.
Sometimes passengers bounce a little as
the train speeds along the track.

In a busy, crowded city like New York,
travel by subway is faster than travel
by car. The trains need not stop for

traffic lights as cars do. They are not
blocked by street traffic, either. They
just bounce along, stopping only to let
passengers get on and off.

Today there are far more freight trains
than passenger trains. Freight trains
carry all kinds of things that people need.

Some of the longest freight trains
have almost a hundred cars. By looking
at the cars of a real train or a toy
train, you see they are not all alike.
Different kinds of cars are used for
different kinds of freight.

On the next two pages you will see
pictures of some of the different kinds
of freight cars.

Find the picture of the stock car.
This car is used to carry horses,
pigs, sheep, and other kinds of stock.
The sides of a stock car have slats with
openings between them. This lets the
animals get fresh air as they travel.

Another car is the tank car. Oil is
one of the things carried in a tank car.
Can you think of other things that could
be carried in a tank car?

The boxcar has a sliding door on each
side. Boxcars carry canned food and
other kinds of goods.

The first car at the bottom of the
last page is a flatcar. Flatcars have
no sides. Logs, cars, and small trucks
may be loaded onto flatcars.

A freight car with a funny name is the
piggy-back car. It can carry a big truck
trailer. The trailer, and whatever is in
it, rides piggy-back right down the track.

At the very end of the train is the
little red caboose. The caboose is home
for the workers on the train. It is
where they rest and eat when they have
time off from their jobs.

A Floating City

All is ready! The big ship blasts its whistle, and people wave. They keep on waving as the whistle blasts again.

"Bon voyage! Bon voyage!" come the shouts. "Have fun and write to me!"

Four or five tugboats pull the ship away. The floating city is on its way.

The big ship leaves the shore behind. In a little while the tugboats turn back. Then the big ship picks up speed and is soon on the open sea.

Life on a big ship is like one holiday after another. As soon as the passengers unpack their bags, they will be ready to have fun.

Those who enjoy swimming will head for the swimming pools. Others will head for the game rooms where they can play many different kinds of games. There are also places on deck where the passengers can sit in the sun and enjoy the cool winds that blow from the sea.

The fun on a big ship does not end when night comes. At night, passengers can go to the movies. Or they can dance, sing, and play more games. With so many ways to enjoy themselves, there are few unhappy people on a big ship.

Have you guessed yet why a big ship
is sometimes called a floating city?
Could it be that on a big ship, just as
in a city, there are many things to do?

In a city you can go to the movies,
swim, and play games. You can go to a
restaurant to eat, and you can go to a
store to shop.

You can do these things on a ship, too.
There are little shops where passengers
buy books, cards, candy, games, and many
other things you can name. And, of course,
there are places where they can eat, even
at midnight if they wish.

If anyone on a big ship is unhappy
because he misses his family back home,
he may call them up. There are even
doctors for those who become sick.

Yes, a ship is like a floating city
all right. It has so many things to do
that some people are unable to do them all.

Some ships are longer than three city blocks. They are almost as long as our tallest buildings are tall.

Big ·ships have four or five decks. They can carry about two thousand people.

Traveling by ship is fun. But it does take time. A five—day trip by ship would take about six hours by plane. So traveling by ship to a far-away country is for those who want to enjoy getting there as much as being there.

From Here to There

America is known for its giant buildings. Some of them are so tall that they seem to scrape the sky. These buildings are called skyscrapers.

Some of America's big buildings aren't skyscrapers. Some are big in another way. They spread over a lot of ground.

In a small building, people walk to get from one part to another. But in big buildings, walking is not the answer. We need other ways of getting around.

This skyscraper in
New York City is a very
tall office building.
It has over one hundred
floors. People can go
from the bottom floor
to the top floor in one
of the many elevators.

Until men learned to
build elevators, there
were no skyscrapers or
tall apartment houses.
Can you guess why?

Most people would
never live or work
in a building if they
had to climb up more
than a few flights
of stairs to get to
an office or to an
apartment.

This odd-looking building is on the West Coast. It is a restaurant which is at the top of the pole. As the people eat, the restaurant turns around. In about an hour, it turns all the way around.

To get to the restaurant, people must get into an outside elevator. The elevator is on the outside of the building so people can look down on the city as they travel up or down.

In most big stores, there are three
ways to go from one floor to the next.
You can walk up a flight of stairs.
You can go up in one of the elevators.
Or you can take an escalator.

An escalator is a moving stairway.
As you see in the drawing, the stairs
are on a moving belt. The belt moves
around and around. To go up, you step
from the floor onto the bottom step.
You can stand on that same step as it
carries you to the next floor.

When you want to go down, you must
get onto another escalator, one that is
moving the other way.

This picture shows another way of
getting from one part of a building to
another part. It is a picture of a
moving sidewalk.

To use a moving sidewalk, people must
step onto a belt which moves them along.
The belt moves about as fast as people
walk. By just standing on the belt, you
can get from one part of a building to
another part.

Elevators, escalators, and moving
sidewalks are useful to people who live,
work, and shop in our big cities. Without
these ways of traveling indoors, we would
have little use for skyscrapers and other
big buildings.

There Are So Many Ways of Going Places

Big yellow trolley
    lumbers along,
Long black subway
    sings an under song.
Airplanes swoop
    and flash in the sky,
Noisy old elevated
    goes rocketing by.
Boats across the water —
    back and forth they go,
Big boats and little boats,
    fast boats and slow.

Trains puff and thunder;
    their engines have a headlight;
They have a special kind of car
    where you can sleep all night.
Tall fat buses on the Avenue,
They will stop for anyone —
    even — just — you.
All kinds of autos rush
    down the street.
And then there are always —
    your own two feet.

LESLIE THOMPSON

Space

When I'm big I want to be
A space cadet so I shall see
All the planets out in space —
I'll be a rocketeer, and ace.

I will fly a rocket ship
Zoom! I'll blast off on a trip
To the moon. Through space I'll fly —
In seas of space, beyond the sky,

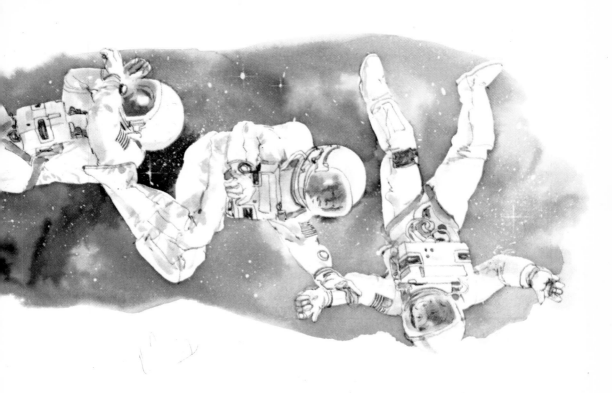

I'll have space suits and helmets, too,
One for each man in the crew,
So we can breathe when we get there.
(Around the moon there is no air.)

When you're on the moon you weigh
Very little—so they say.
So we'll bounce around and then
We'll zoom back to earth again.

INEZ HOGAN

Can You Read This?

What Makes a Rocket Go Up?

Fire and smoke and hot <u>gases</u> flash out from the rocket. Some people think that the rocket goes up because the hot gases <u>push</u> the air <u>aside</u>. This isn't so.

You can see for yourself what makes a rocket go. All you need is a chair that can slide on the floor.

Sit in the chair. Hold onto it. <u>Bend</u> your <u>knees</u>, and pull them up close to your body. Now, get ready to <u>straighten</u> out your legs quickly. Get ready to push your feet away from your body as fast as you can.

Ready? Push!

What happened to the chair? Did you notice the chair move?

Try it again. Bend your knees. Pull your feet up close to your body. Push your

224

feet away, fast. The chair moves back. Not far, but it does move.

What has this to do with a rocket? A rocket moves in the same way that the chair moves. When you push your feet away, something else happens. You push your body the other way. Pushing your feet <u>forward</u> pushes your body and your chair <u>backward</u> You push your feet away, and your feet push you away.

This is just the sort of thing that happens to a rocket. The rocket pushes hot gases away. The hot gases push the rocket away. The rocket pushes the gases one way. The gases push the rocket the other way. The push has nothing to do with the air, you see. This is why rockets will work in <u>space</u>, where there is no air.

1. What does this selection tell you?
2. Is this a "make-believe" or an "informational" selection?

When You Read

(To be read with the teacher)

Studying New Words

These words were in the selection you just read. Can you read these words now?

gases	bend	straighten
push	knees	forward
aside	space	backward

The word **gases** is a plural form. What suffix makes **gases** a plural form? How many vowel sounds do you hear in **gases**?

Which other word is a plural form? What is the vowel sound in this word? What letters stand for this vowel sound?

What does **straight** mean? What does **straighten** mean?

Two of the words have opposite meanings. What two parts of these words are the same? Use each word in a sentence.

What two letters stand for the last sound in **push**? Do the last two letters in **bend** stand for one sound or for two?

Look at the words _aside and **space**. Which word has two syllables? What is the vowel sound in the first syllable? What is the vowel sound in the second syllable? What letter pattern stands for this sound? What is the vowel sound in the word with one syllable? What letter pattern stands for the vowel sound in **space**?

When you read a word that is new to you, you must look carefully at the letters in the word. You look for letter patterns. You think of the sounds that the letters and the letter patterns stand for. You read the word with the other words in the sentence. If the words make sense together, you have read the word correctly.

Try This

Read each sentence. Tell how you figured out the word and its meaning.

1. Put these books on the bookshelf.
2. The fishermen went fishing early this morning.
3. Ted is the friendliest boy I ever met.
4. The little girl put the pieces of the puzzle together by herself.
5. The bird flew into the air.
6. A cold drink tastes good on a hot day.

Now read this paragraph. Then tell how you figured out how to say each underlined word. Tell how you knew the meaning of each underlined word.

The fishermen climbed aboard the fishing boat, and the boat headed toward the open sea. The men would soon be tossing out their nets. They hoped to catch enough fish to earn a day off from work.

A Time for Flowers

by Mark Taylor

Illustrations by Graham Booth

It was a day of shining sun. It was a day of bright flowers. But it was a day when Taro and his sister Michi had a big unhappiness.

"Why do my two little ones look so long of face?" asked Grandfather.

"Father will not let us help in the flower fields," said Michi. "He says we are too little."

"He will not let us go to the Flower Market with him," said Taro. "He says we are too little."

Grandfather, who was older and wiser than anyone, smiled. "Too little is too little," he said, "and it is hard to be too little."

"But I don't feel too little," said Taro.

"I don't feel too little either," Michi agreed.

"Someday when you are bigger," said Grandfather, "you will be able to get up in the middle of the night and ride in the truck to the big city far away. It is a long trip to the Flower Market. But now you are—"

"Too little," said Taro.

"You are too little for the Flower Market," said Grandfather, "but I think you are big enough for something else."

"Big enough for what?" asked Taro.

"Big enough to make a garden just your size," said Grandfather.

"What size will that be?" asked Michi.

"The right size," said Grandfather. He showed them how to make a garden. Together they made it behind the barn. And while they

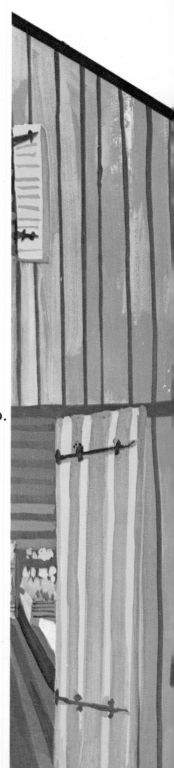

made the garden, Grandfather told
them stories about Japan where he
lived as a little boy.

"The world is a place of many wonders,"
Grandfather said. "Best of all its wonders
are flowers and butterflies—and children.
They always make me want to laugh and dance."

"If only we could go to the Flower
Market," sighed Taro, "then I would laugh
and sing and dance—and jump right over
the mountain!"

"For that you are too little," said Michi.

Every day Taro and Michi took care of
the garden and watched the plants grow.
Sometimes it would rain. Grandfather said
that was a very good thing for flowers.

Most of the time the sun would shine.
Grandfather said that, too, was a very
good thing for flowers. So the garden
grew and grew.

At last a day came when Taro's and Michi's garden was blazing with bright flowers. They picked some to show to Grandfather at dinner time. Father and Mother and big brother Mike were very proud of Taro and Michi.

"This is something to dance about!" Grandfather laughed. Together he and Taro and Michi danced. They danced so hard that Grandfather's glasses bounced right off his nose and smashed on the floor!

The children knew that Grandfather could hardly see without his glasses. Without his glasses how could he see the things he loved best—the mountains and the flowers and the sea?

Father said they would take Grandfather to buy a new pair. "No, no, not now," said Grandfather. "There isn't enough money to buy new glasses for an old man."

It was terrible. Grandfather said there was not enough money. Taro and Michi didn't know what to do.

After dinner Taro had an idea which he told to Michi. "We will ask Father to sell our flowers at the Flower Market. We will give the money to Grandfather for new glasses," he explained.

Michi was glad. It would be a surprise for Grandfather.

They asked Father if he would sell their flowers, but they didn't tell him about the plan.

"Sure, I will sell your flowers in the Flower Market," said Father. "I will take them with me in the morning, if you get them ready. What will you do with the money?"

"A big secret," said Taro.

"A good secret," said Michi.

"That's the best kind of secret," said Father.

Taro and Michi carefully packed their flowers in a big basket and gave it to Father before they went to bed. But they were worried. With so many flowers to sell, would Father remember to take theirs?

In the middle of the night, Taro and Michi decided to make sure their flowers were in the truck. They had to be as careful as two mice. It was not allowed to be up at night. They climbed in the back of the truck. It was filled with hundreds and hundreds of flowers.

While they were still looking for their basket, something surprising happened. Father climbed into the truck and started it up. Taro and Michi were too scared to speak.

The next thing they knew, the truck was on its way to the Flower Market. And so were they!

"I'm scared," said Michi. "What will happen to us?"

"I don't know," said Taro. "We need a new plan."

So Taro thought for a long time as the truck bounced and bumped and roared down the freeway. While he was thinking, Michi found their basket of flowers.

"I have a plan," Taro finally said. "We will sneak out of the truck with our flowers. We will sell them ourselves. We will have to sell our flowers and get back in the truck before Father sees us."

When the truck stopped at last, Taro and Michi held their breaths. As quickly as two frightened spiders, they let themselves down from the truck. They carried their basket of flowers.

The street was crowded with trucks and people and big buildings and millions of flowers everywhere. So this was the Flower Market!

242

Taro and Michi kept out of Father's
sight. They were pretty frightened, but
they watched how Father took the flowers
from the truck and put them on big stands
inside a big building. Then Father stood
by his flowers and people came to buy them.
Everywhere there were hundreds of flower
stands and hundreds of people selling
flowers just like Father.

Taro and Michi knew just what to do. They found an old board and, in a place where Father would not see them, they made a stand of their own.

But nobody noticed Taro and Michi. Nobody bought their flowers. All Taro and Michi could see were millions of bright flowers and thousands of busy feet.

244

When two of the feet
stopped right in front
of them, Taro and Michi
looked up. A big man
was staring down at them.

"What are you doing
here?" he asked in a
stern voice.

"Selling flowers," said Taro.

"You aren't allowed
to sell flowers here,
did you know that?"
said the man. "Where
do you children belong?"

"Home," whispered Michi.

"Who are you?" said Taro.

"I'm a guard," said the
man. "Bring your basket
and come with me."

Taro and Michi were in
bad trouble.

246

The guard took them to an office high above the Flower Market. A man was there, sitting behind a desk. When the man found out their name, he told the guard to get their father.

Taro and Michi were miserable. Their plan was ruined. Father would be very angry! What would happen next?

When Father came he was very angry indeed. "It was wrong of you to hide in the truck when I told you you were too little to come to the Flower Market," he said.

"It was an accident," answered Taro in a small voice. "We didn't mean to."

"We only did it for Grandfather," Michi cried.

"You had better explain," said Father.

So Taro told all about their plans for getting money to buy new glasses for Grandfather.

"I understand now," Father said when Taro had finished. "You were brave children. Of course I will always sell your flowers for you. You should have known I wouldn't forget."

"I would like to buy Taro's and Michi's basket of flowers today," said the man behind the desk. "They are the best I ever saw."

So everything turned out well after all. Taro and Michi were happy. Then it was time to go home, but first they went to a restaurant and had pancakes for breakfast.

Grandfather and Mother and Mike were overjoyed to see Taro and Michi safe and snug with Father.

"How we worried," Mother told them.

Grandfather was very happy when Taro and Michi told him about the plan to earn money for his new glasses. But they promised that never again would they sneak out in the middle of the night.

Afterwards, Grandfather and Taro and Michi went out to their garden. When nobody was looking, guess what?

They danced!

Taro and Michi and Grandfather sang and danced.

And Taro jumped—but not over the mountain. "For that," he said, "I am really too little."

252

THE VOCABULARY

Most words in *Going Places, Seeing People*, the 2-2 Reader in THE BOOKMARK READING PROGRAM, are introduced to pupils before they meet them in this book. These words are taught either in *Reading Skills Six* or are introduced by the teacher before the story is read. Those words which children can identify independently are designated as Attack Words. All words introduced at previous levels, except for a few special nouns, are repeated in *Going Places, Seeing People*. Compound words made up of two known words are not identified as new words. Variant forms of familiar words are not listed when they are formed with suffixes that have been taught. (See the accompanying Teacher's Edition for a further discussion of the vocabulary in the Primary Readers of THE BOOKMARK READING PROGRAM.)

Starred words are taught in Word Service lessons that immediately precede the story in which they appear. These words illustrate the particular phonic or structural element taught in the lessons.

Unstarred words are taught in the teaching plan preceding the reading of the story. These words contain either irregular patterns or patterns that have not yet been taught.

Attack words are met for the first time in the context of the story. Pupils can identify these words in context by applying their knowledge of phonics and structure.

UNIT I
7. different
faces*

8. . . . .
9. . . . .
10. sister
our
late*
11. does
always
12. any
pale*
windows
13. . . . .
14. afraid*

15. (*Poem*)

16. lollipop
Glen Dee
17. high*
shine*
18. sigh*
bagpipes
Janet
19. fire*
sight*
20. . . . .
21. . . . .
22. . . . .

23. Mabuna's
village
jungle

24. bananas
25. hold*
26. most*
27. woke*
28. scold*
told*

29. Tito's
mountains
Mexico
wind
30. market
31. finest*
32. smallest*
narrow
33. hair
longest*
34. proudest*

35. sea*
36. Tonio
37. son*
pail*
38. brothers
their*
39. there*

40. shiny*
41. . . . .
42. . . . .
43. . . . .
44.
45. . . . .

46. adobe

47. walls*
floor
48. close*
49. plaza
50. ready
here

51. Eagle Feather
Navajo
52. . . . .
53. Teasing Boy
corral
54. horse
55. hogan
hurt
56. jacket*
skirt
fur
57. . . . .
58. been

59. (*Poem*)

60. (*Skills*
61. *Lesson*)
62.
63.
64.

UNIT II
65. dragons
giants

66. believe
stories*
know*

67. forest
knew*
68. . . . .
69. . . . .
70. Mushrush
horns
71. knight*

72. castle
Sir Charles
73. terrible
fear*
roar
clear*
dear*
74. wizard
change
bottle
75. hear*
76. . . . .
77. bottom
78. near*
79. holiday
80. . . . .

81. . . . .
82. millions
dinosaurs
83. claws*
almost*
also*
84. lizard
even
85. tongue
jaws*

255

ATTACK WORDS

Pages 8–14
grand

Pages 16–22
stone
sheep
honking

Pages 23–28
chattered
bite
kept
alone
men

Pages 29–34
town
pole
wide
standing
seemed

Pages 35–45
fish
supper
sand
deep
tide
pool
boats
fresh
mean
sold

Pages 46–50
bricks
strong
plastered
smooth
feel
feasting
shut

Pages 51–58
drove
goats
skin
hi
gate
mouths
smoke
post

Pages 66–71
teeth
sting
snake
kill
brave
gold

Pages 72–80
flag
waved
rode
pocket
asleep

Pages 81–85
kites
hunt
bones

Pages 86–90
whales
chin
swim

Pages 92–97
Jack
cow
spade
ax
pit
blast

dare
smashed
ate

Pages 98–107
wife
queen
find
scare
fed
hate
tears

Pages 108–11
those
nose
draw
barn
might
these

Pages 118–22
stamp
cards

Pages 123–28
understand

Pages 129–32
save
flat
U.S.
much
cost
such
dime

Pages 133–37
shore
snail
clam
junk

Pages 138–41
kits
wise
life

Pages 148–52
tales
sneaked

Pages 153–58
beet
sell
cart
stare
agreed
greedy
speak

Pages 159–62
jam
dinner
crow

Pages 163–67
voice
stove
wrong

Pages 168–72
butterflies
while

Pages 173–85
bench
watch
mice
midnight
tap
outfits
snug
pants
sang

Pages 194–97
report
east
wouldn't
spot
west
blaze

Pages 198–202
blades
airports
train

Pages 203–09
along
track
alike
goods
speed
coast
hours
railroad
stairs
bounce
stock
between
tank
canned

Pages 210–14
ship
tugboats
deck
become

Pages 215–19
scrape
skyscraper
aren't
flights
belt
step

2
3
4
5
6
7
8
9

D
E
F
G
H
I
J